PRIMER IN ORGANIC CHEMISTRY
Dr. Butcher's Paradigms for a Quarter
(Don't be Short-changed)

JARED BUTCHER
Ohio University

WILEY
CUSTOM SERVICES

Printed in the United States of America.

10 9 8 7 6 5 4 3 2 1

ISBN 0-471-32455-8

Dr. Butcher's Paradigms for a Quarter (Don't be short-changed.)

paradigm EXAMPLE, PATTERN (Webster's Dictionary)

Preface

This primer is intended to help you learn organic chemistry. It was my original intention to produce a document that would tell you the minimum you needed to know to be a good fake, but it turns out that even a good fake requires an understanding of almost everything at once, so the primer evolved into its present form. Looking at it will teach you what to look for in your textbook. Practically every chapter in every textbook assumes you know the material in this primer. Look for it. Keep the big picture in mind and try to relate the ideas, one to the other, through the ideas given below. Organic is not a Mickey Mouse course. In fact, for most students, it is less like Mickey and Pluto and more like Dante's Inferno! Organic Chemistry requires the use of both sides of the brain – the artistic, graphic, non-verbal right side, as well as the verbal left side. What tends to make matters worse is that both sides must communicate with each other simultaneously. Information must be transmitted from one side of the brain to the other and back often and repeatedly. This is how it works: I will draw a picture on the board for you. I will see in it what I believe to be important. You will see the picture and attempt to copy it down and in your notes you place what you think is important. If we agree, then the information transfers. If the transfer fails, then you are frustrated and so am I. The course then becomes a trip through Hell and my name takes on added significance.... (I would prefer that my name were "Virgil." He was Dante's guide through the Inferno. He didn't make it Hell, but he guided Dante through it, and Dante got through it unscathed. That is my wish for you.)

The most important part of our experience in the next few weeks is honesty. It is important that you be honest with your teacher and with yourself. You will be challenged by tests designed to measure your progress in this class. The results will be presented to you with all sincerity and you should act on the result with the enthusiasm you would have if you had given the test to yourself. In the end, your grade will be your teacher's honest opinion of your ability to learn the subject material. If that does not match your own opinion, then you will be unhappy with your grade. Read on to see how to avoid that catastrophe.

How to Think, How to Read, and How to Study Organic Chemistry

The Acquisition of Power

Let's face it – Organic Chemistry is all about power: gaining power to get into medical school, controlling power to get into graduate school, using power to get (and keep) a good job. When a teacher lectures, it means: "I have the power." When a teacher says, "This is the way that goes," it is a declaration of power. Where does this power come from? How can you get some?

The power comes through the use of language (metaphor) and as long as you can keep the language from changing, you can keep the power. That is why textbooks encourage you to learn the vocabulary and definitions without innovations. The language cannot change, or power is lost. That is the reason why "reasonable-sounding" answers get marked wrong. The other reason why answers get marked wrong is the professor's argument that, "I use the language better than you do; therefore, I have the right to power." As a student, your only recourse against such "tyranny" is to learn the language and use it as well as your teacher does. Completely master the language of the discipline and earn a Master's Degree; control the language better than your professors and earn a Ph.D. I expect this declaration holds for any discipline, but I know it works in chemistry.

Organic chemistry is made particularly difficult by the fact that everything is done in pictures. Every line and every dot that composes these pictures provides part of the metaphor of organic chemistry. Mastering the use of dots, lines, and curved arrows means mastering the language of the discipline. If the lecture strikes you as being abstract, then it is probably because your teacher uses the language in a way that you do not understand. This does not mean that you can't master it, but only that you haven't yet. Study.

There are many problems with these pictures. The first is a question of the functional groups they contain. The functional groups have names and structures, and in order to master this language you need to know where every electron is and how to represent it in a picture. You will also need to know when to draw a functional group out and when to abbreviate it. Watch your professor; read your book. Learn to do as they do. Learning how to learn is the point of education, and this is a good way to start. Organic chemistry provides the challenge of learning something entirely new and learning it in a totally different way. Your teacher's role is to provide guidance and direction during the process, to assess your progress toward this goal, and to evaluate your success after you have finished the course.

An excerpt from "Drawing on the Right Side of the Brain" by Betty Edwards (used with permission of the copyright holder: J. P. Tarcher, Inc.)

THE TWO MODES OF INFORMATION PROCESSING

Inside each of our skulls, therefore, we have a double brain with two ways of knowing. The dualities and differing characteristics of the two halves of the brain and body, intuitively expressed in our language, have a real basis in the physiology of the human brain. Because the connecting fibers are intact in normal brains, we rarely experience at a conscious level conflicts revealed by the tests on split-brain patients.

Nevertheless, as each of our hemispheres gathers in the same sensory information, each half of our brains may handle the information in different ways: the task may be divided between the hemispheres, each handling the part suited to its style. Or one hemisphere, often the dominant left, will "take over" and inhibit the other half. The left hemisphere analyzes, abstracts, counts, marks time, plans step-by-step procedures, verbalizes, makes rational statements based on logic. For example, "Given numbers *a, b,* and *c* -- existing only in the mind's eye -- or recall things that may be real (can you image your front door, for example?). We see how things exist in space and how the parts go together to make up the whole. Using the right hemisphere, we understand metaphors, we dream, we create new combinations of ideas. When something is too complex to describe, we can make gestures that communicate. Psychologist David Galin has a favorite example: try to describe a spiral staircase *without* making a spiral gesture. And using the right hemisphere we are able to draw pictures of our perceptions.

The Ah-ha! Response

In the right-hemisphere mode of information processing, we use intuition and have leaps of insight -- moments when "everything seems to fall into place" without figuring things out in a logical order. When this occurs, people often spontaneously exclaim, "I've got it" or "Ah, yes, now I see the picture." The classic example of this kind of exclamation is the exultant cry, "Eureka!" (*I have found it!*) attributed to Archimedes. According to the story, Archimedes experienced a flash of insight while bathing that enabled him to formulate his principle of using the weight of displaced water to determine the weight of solid objects.

This, then, is the right-hemisphere mode: the intuitive, subjective, relational, holistic, time-free mode. This is also the disdained, weak, left-handed mode which in our culture has been generally ignored. For example, most of our educational system has been designed to cultivate the verbal, rational, on-time left hemisphere, while half of the brain of every student is virtually neglected.

2

HALF A BRAIN IS BETTER THAN NONE:
A WHOLE BRAIN WOULD BE BETTER

With their sequenced verbal and numerical classes, the schools you and I attended were not equipped to teach the right-hemisphere mode. The right hemisphere is not, after all, under very good verbal control. You can't reason with it. You can't get it to make logical propositions such as "This is good and that is bad, for *a*, *b*, and *c* reasons." It is metaphorically *left-handed*, with all the ancient connotations of that characteristic. The right hemisphere is not good at sequencing -- doing the first thing first, taking the next step, then the next. It may start anywhere, or take everything at once. Furthermore, the right hemisphere hasn't a good sense of time and doesn't seem to comprehend what is meant by the term "wasting time" as does the good, sensible left hemisphere. The right brain is not good at categorizing and naming. It seems to regard the thing as-it-is, at the present moment of the present; seeing things for what they simply are, in all of their awesome, fascinating complexity. It is not good at analyzing and abstracting salient characteristics.

Even today, though educators are increasingly concerned with the importance of intuitive and creative thought, school systems in general are still structured in the left-hemisphere mode. Teaching is sequenced: students progress through grades one, two, three, etc., in a linear direction. The main subjects learners study are verbal and numerical: reading, writing, arithmetic. Time schedules are followed. Seats are set in rows. Learners converge on answers. Teachers give out grades. And everyone senses that something is amiss.

The right brain -- the dreamer, the artificer, the artist -- is lost in our school system and goes largely untaught. We might find a few art classes, a few shop classes, something called "creative writing," and perhaps courses in music; but it's unlikely that we would find courses in imagination, in visualization, in perceptual or spatial skills, in creativity as a separate subject, in intuition, in inventiveness. Yet educators value these skills and have apparently hoped that students would develop imagination, perception, and intuition as natural consequences of a training in verbal, analytic skills.

Fortunately, such development often does occur almost in spite of the school system -- a tribute to the survival capacity of the right brain. But the emphasis of our culture is so strongly slanted toward rewarding left-brain skills that we are surely losing a very large proportion of the potential ability of the other halves of our children's brains. Scientist Jerre Levy has said -- only partly humorously -- that American scientific training through graduate school may entirely *destroy* the right hemisphere. We certainly are aware of the effects of inadequate training in verbal, computational skills. The verbal left hemisphere never seems to recover fully, and the effects may handicap students for life. What happens, then, to the right hemisphere which is hardly trained at all?

Perhaps now that neuroscientists have provided a conceptual base for right-brain training, we can begin to build a school system that will teach the whole brain. Such a system will surely include training in drawing skills -- an efficient, effective way to gain access to right-brain functions.

How Thinking Works

To my knowledge, there are four ways of thinking about things: Intuitive, Concrete, Formal and Topological. Intuitive thinking means guessing. Sometimes this works, they tell me, but in my personal experience it always fails when you use it on an exam. Of course, when you are working on the cutting-edge of research, and there is nothing else to guide you, guessing becomes the only option. In those cases, we invoke the "Scientific Method" and claim our guess to be a hypothesis. In ordinary life, an intuitive thinker can be amazing. They will jump to the correct conclusion, but then they can't explain why it is correct or how they happened to pick that answer. Concrete thinking isn't really thinking as much as it is memory. It is based on the memory of learned examples. Once they have seen a problem worked, students who use concrete thinking can work that problem, and if they can remember enough worked examples they can score well on tests. It is not an efficient method and it takes a tremendous memory to be effective, but I have seen this work for some people. This level of thinking is expected of students in high school. Formal thinking is expected of college students. Here one reasons by analogy. In organic chemistry, when the abbreviation R-turns up, formal thinking is called for. Analogy built up on a basis of fact: "This ester will react that way because all esters react that way." It is very useful to think by analogy. Once you begin thinking in the formal mode, then the curved arrow formalism will start making sense to you and you will excel. I see it happen all the time. A student will go from wanting to see every atom and every electron in a molecule one day to using R-groups and curved arrows the next and the performance on exams doubles. Topological thinking is reasoning by analogies based on other analogies which have their basis in fact. A topological thinker moves from idea to idea with a rapidity that looks like intuition, but if questioned it is like they can pull out a pocket watch and give your the time of day. They back up every step by using formal analogies, or concrete examples. It is amazing. Occasionally a students tell me "you would have to be a Ph.D. to be able to think like that." A Ph.D. is no guarantee that a person is a topological thinker, but we are in the business to help the topological thinkers become Ph.D.s, and I am thinking about *you* as I write this.

Creativity in Chemistry

If organic chemistry is an art form, an idea I will elaborate later, then the study of organic chemistry is really about creativity and the appreciation of creativity. It is important for you to be able to distinguish between the competent and mediocre and the creative and stellar. Here are some things you might want to consider. I call them four types of creativity: The first is the correction of an old error. If something has been accepted for a long time, it becomes part of the paradigm. If it is wrong and someone can prove that it is wrong, that constitutes creativity. Watch for it. It will be mentioned in your textbook. The second type of creativity is the introduction of a new paradigm. Scientific research goes on in other disciplines outside organic. Things like chromatography and NMR that were developed by others have become the standard procedure for us today. There was a time when all an organic chemist had was melting point and elemental analysis. We all owe a great debt to those courageous individuals who showed us something new. They were creative. The third type of creativity I will high light is competence, or improved precision of measurement. In my last point, I mentioned elemental analysis. It was brought to us by a competent individual who might have been considered mediocre except that he brought a creative new method of analysis. My personal favorite method of creativity is the discovery. It is the most rare and perfect method of introducing a new paradigm, or correcting an old error that it stands in a class by itself. If you discover one thing in your professional career it will probably be the most memorable thing in your life. Cherish it. Watch for it in the textbook. Pasteur's resolution of chiral crystals is in this category.

Four Premises

Four premises form the basis for this primer: 1. Fundamental concepts explain everything in organic chemistry and that if you understand them, then you can figure out everything else; 2. Mathematics provides the confidence to make predictions and if you can identify all of the elements and operations mathematically, then learning the material is enjoyable; 3. Paradigms are working models that can be used to solve problems. (A scientist objects to the words: *metaphor* and *bias,* and I object to the word *prejudice,* but a paradigm is all of these things. The body of knowledge that has built up in organic chemistry is a collection of paradigms. Use them, and solve problems.) 4. Creation of Art is the purpose of life.

1. Fundamental concepts explain everything in organic chemistry

This course will be greatly simplified if you can tolerate the formal method of thinking, because there are four concepts that apply to everything you will study. Granted, they may apply in different ways in each application, but they are grounded in fact and they go a long way toward explaining everything. They are (1) the Inductive Effect (σ-system); (2) the Resonance Effect (π-system); (3) the Change in Hybridization; and (4) the Influence of Neighboring Groups. It does seem strange that four factors would explain everything, but let us test this hypothesis and see how far it will carry us. In each example or problem, stop and ask yourself how each one applies. I will give you concrete examples below, but one or more of them can be applied in every case. Before we can begin, we have to understand all of the words and symbols.

The Inductive Effect

When two atoms share a pair of electrons, it makes a covalent bond. If the two atoms are identical, the bond is not polarized, but if the atoms are different, then one atom will have a greater electrostatic attraction for the electrons. This polarizes the bond by making the more electronegative element carry a partial negative charge; the more electropositive element carry a partial positive charge. This is the inductive effect. A difference in electronegativity induces partial charges on the atoms. This effect works through the (σ-system), so it is important whenever atoms are bound to each other. That means it is important all of the time. Here are some examples in which the inductive effect is really important. One example is hydrogen bonding. When a hydrogen is bound to an electronegative element like oxygen, the σ-bond becomes strongly polarized. It is not enough for a formal charge, but it is a lot. The partial + charge (δ+) on the hydrogen and the partial - charge (δ-) on the oxygen form a dipole. (That's what polarized means: a dipole (δ+ & δ-) is induced in a σ-bond by a difference in electronegativity. Does this mean it would be worthwhile to memorize a table of electronegativity values? You bet it does! Start with H, C, N, O and F, then learn Cl, Br, S and I. Notice that by the time you get to sulfur and iodine, the electronegativity is the same as it is for carbon, but we still think of them as electronegative elements. Finally, learn Li, Mg, B, Al and Si. That should last a lifetime. Others can be looked up as needed. Hydrogen bonding (H-bonding) is our first example of the inductive effect. It is really important for inorganic molecules (like HF and H_2O), but organic molecules (like alcohols and amines), and biological molecules (like proteins and DNA), all owe their special properties to H-bonding. H-bonding results from the Inductive Effect and that effect can be attributed to differences in electronegativity between the atoms joined by the S_N2 reaction. Here is a reaction that was studied so much that we now know a lot about its mechanism. (A mechanism is analogous to the working part of a machine. In organic chemistry it serves as a metaphor for the workings of a chemical reaction.) The S_N2 reaction can be attributed directly to the inductive effect. The difference in electronegativity between the carbon and the electronegativity of the atom in the leaving-group induces a partial + charge (δ+) on the carbon and a δ- on the electronegative atom in the leaving group. The nucleophile (N in S_N2) loves a + charge. (-phile in nucleophile and Phil- in Philadelphia both come from love. Philadelphia is the city of brotherly love, and a nucleophile loves a nucleus because the nucleus is where the + charge resides. a nucleophile has a pair of electrons to share with the nucleus of another atom. This is another metaphor, isn't it?) In the case of S_N2, the nucleophile comes in at the same time the leaving-group leaves, so there would seem that both, the nucleophile and the leaving group, are coupled to the carbon at the same time. The 2 in S_N2 is used to indicate that both nucleophile and leaving group are involved at the same time. Of course, the S in S_N2 stands for substitution and in this case that means that the nucleophile substitutes for the leaving-group. This is a flawed concept, because the nucleophile always comes in on the opposite side of the carbon while the leaving-group leaves. So in fact, the substitution gives inversion of configuration; a process that changes R to S, or cis to trans. This is a topic in stereochemistry, and it doesn't really involve the inductive effect. All the inductive effect did was to make the S_N2 reaction possible by building up a δ+ on the carbon attached to the leaving-group.

Acidity

The inductive effect causes protons to become acidic when they are involved directly, or indirectly, with electronegative elements. The inductive effect pulls electron density away from an atom. A proton has no other source of electrons besides its σ-bond, so if those electrons are pulled away, it will become acidic finding electron density from other sources. Those other sources are called bases. There are competing theories about acids and bases, but Lewis bases are atoms having a pair of electrons available for bonding. The confusing part is that a nucleophile was defined above as an atom having a pair of electrons to share with the nucleus of another atom. This is not a contradiction. A nucleophile often acts as a base, and a base often acts as a nucleophile. The case that causes the most confusion is the E2 reaction. It is easy to understand that the inductive effect makes the proton in water acidic because the oxygen atom is hogging the electrons, but in the E2 reaction, the proton is attached to a carbon. Here the explanation is that the inductive effect reaches through the σ-system from the electronegative atom to the carbon in a way that makes the carbon pull electron density away from the proton. How could this be? Well, the leaving-group induces a δ+ on the carbon to which it is attached. (You remember, this is the δ+ that made the S_N2 reaction possible.) This δ+ also pulls electron density away from the carbon attached to it and induces a δ+ on it. This δ+ is responsible for pulling the electron density away from the proton and making it acidic. As a result the base can pull the proton off and this causes the elimination to occur. Since the leaving group is lost at the same time the base is pulling off the proton, this reaction also involves two molecules at once and this aspect is reported by the 2 in E2. Both S_N2 and E2 are called concerted reactions because more than two electrons move in concert, that is, at the same time. There are two general notions here that link the inductive effect to acidity. The first is that a proton attached to an electronegative element, like oxygen, is acidic. The second is that a proton on a carbon bearing a partial + charge, or even on the carbon next to a carbon with a δ+ is acidic. If this partial + charge were a formal + charge, then the proton would be even more acidic and that is observed. These results can be generalized and classified into standard mechanistic steps and this can be found under that heading.

Spectroscopy

The best and most sensitive instrument for measuring electron density around a nucleus is NMR. It turns out that the inductive effect drastically influences the position of a signal (chemical shift) for a proton, or carbon. In general, the higher the partial + charge, the farther downfield (that is, away from the reference standard: TMS) the resonance will occur. TMS, tetramethylsilane is a molecule having a carbon-silicon bond that is polarized by the inductive effect in favor of carbon because carbon is more electronegative than silicon. This means that the electron density around the carbon, and around the protons attached to it, is as great as could possibly be had. Electrons moving in a magnetic field create a magnetic field of their own that opposes the external field and shields the nucleus from its influence to a small extent. In this case, that small extent is at its maximum and the signals for both the protons and the carbon occur at the upfield extreme in the spectra. Since it is out of the way, it was chosen as the standard. What could be better? A methyl group attached to a carbon gives a signal downfield from TMS and a methyl group attached to an oxygen is farther downfield. Having two oxygens attached forces the carbon to be a methylene instead of methyl, and the signal for it is still farther downfield. The aldehyde group has a carbon in a carbonyl. That gives a double dose of the inductive effect and a change in hybridization to sp^2, consequently the signals for both the proton and the carbon is at the downfield extreme. The changes in the NMR spectra as a result of the inductive effect is a general trend in both ^1H NMR and ^{13}C. The actual numbers vary, but the concept remains resolutely unchanged.

The Resonance Effect

A molecule containing a π-system, a string of sp^2 hybrid atoms, is capable of exhibiting resonance because electrons can flow through the atoms like an electric current in a wire. The result is one in which the electrons are delocalized, or spread out, over more than one atom. If there is a charge, that charge is delocalized, too. This means that the molecule is more stable because the burden of carrying the charge is shared by more than one atom and the cost in energy is reduced. The resonance effect is a term used to describe the influence this delocalization exerts on molecules and reactive intermediates. It is beneficial in every instance save one: anti-aromatic molecules are destabilized by resonance. Conversely, the greatest effect is felt in aromatic compounds. A benzene ring is like a room-temperature superconductor. Electrons race around the ring and generate a magnetic field. That field opposes the external magnetic field from the magnet used in the instrument and it produces a effect in the spectrum that is characteristic of aromatic compounds. The protons attached to the aromatic ring are in the deshielding cone and move downfield (away from TMS) from 4-5 ppm to 7-8 ppm. It is a manifestation of the resonance effect.

The resonance effect can also be used to explain the acidity of a proton in a carboxylic acid group. Here, the two oxygens both contribute in the inductive effect, but once the proton is lost the negative charge is spread over both of the oxygens by resonance. The resonance effect applies to the enolate anion and in the allyl system by formal analogy. The difference in each of these cases is the number and accessibility of the electronegative oxygen atom. On an exam, the question of the influence of the resonance effect should always occur to you. It is second in importance only to the inductive effect. Sometimes they work together as in the case of activating o,p-directors for second substitution on aromatic rings. Sometimes they work against each other, as in the case of de-activating o,p-directors like halogenated aromatic rings. This is a powerful concept. Watch for it.

Changes in Hybridization

In some reactions, the hybridization of an atom changes from sp^2 to sp^3 (the "tetrahedral mechanism") and in others it changes from sp^3 to sp^2 (S_N1). These are important changes and they make memorization easier. They also cause important changes in stereochemistry because an sp^2 hybrid is a flat atom and it can be approached from either side to give a stereorandom product mixture. The differences in hybridization are also apparent in the spectra of compounds. In IR, the sp^3 hybrid atoms all exhibit stretching absorptions in the same general region regardless of whether it is a C-H, an O-H, or an N-H stretch. Similarly, the sp^2 atoms have stretching frequencies grouped together. This fact, combined with an accurate table of data, makes interpreting the spectra relatively easy. In NMR, the effect is even more pronounced. Unless there is some strong inductive effect the signals in NMR divide naturally according to the hybridization: sp^3 in the upfield half of the spectrum and sp^2 in the downfield half. This applies equally well in ^1H and ^{13}C NMR spectra. Look for it.

The perceptive reader will wonder what has happened to sp hybrids. Well, the answer is that these are confusing. Their position in each spectrum can be predicted with certainty, but the reason for its placement is complicated. I will leave that to your textbook.

The Effect of Neighboring Groups

In a reaction mechanism, it is sometimes the influence of the neighboring group that is more important than the reactive center. Carbonyls make protons on the sp^3 carbons to which they are attached much more acidic through a combination of the inductive and resonance effects. An aromatic ring is a neighbor that will make hydrogens attached to an sp^3 carbon attached to them susceptible to H• abstraction owing to the resonance effect. In fact, it is very common for a neighboring group to influence the chemistry of the carbon to which it is attached. Consider the effect of the leaving group on the reactive center in the S_N2 reaction, for example. In NMR, it is the number of protons attached to the neighboring carbon that determines the number of lines in the splitting pattern for the proton of interest, and carbons can often be identified by counting the hydrogens attached to them. In short, consider the neighbor any time you are contemplating a reaction mechanism or a spectroscopy problem. It can't hurt, and often that analysis will provide the answer when nothing else does.

Summary:

These four factors: the inductive effect, the resonance effect, the change in hybridization, and the effect of neighboring groups apply to every problem of structure, mechanism, or spectroscopy. Neither, by itself is sufficient. Use them all, together, every time.

2. Mathematics provides the confidence to make predictions

You probably don't see organic chemistry as a type of mathematics, and who could blame you for that? The truth is that there is an element of abstract algebra in organic chemistry. In abstract algebra there is a restricted set of elements, in organic we consider these as functional groups, and in algebra there is a limited number of operations which we would call reactions. If we could get a grip on these functional groups and the reactions that they do we could use that information to make predictions. There are standard sets of information that cover all of these topics: Electron-dot structures and the rules of resonance used to build up the functional groups, the functional groups themselves, and the standard set of mechanistic steps used to manipulate them. There are some reactions that are so famous that they have names, and these deserve special consideration. Furthermore, there is a standard set of experiments that are used to determine the mechanism of an organic reaction and that list should be memorized and readily available for all emergencies. This is what will be introduced below, and although it doesn't look too much like your math class, I think it will help to think of it in those terms.

Electron-Dot Structures & Rules of Resonance

The most interesting thing I learned in biology was "The Rule of 2 & 8." This rule states that two electrons are needed around each hydrogen and eight around each first row element in a molecule. Armed with this knowledge you can draw molecule and functional groups. One problem is that there are frequently multiple structures which could be correct for molecules like carbon monoxide, and in order to know which of these is correct you need the following:

Rules of resonance
1. Maximize the number of covalent bonds
2. Minimize charge separation
3. Put the negative charge on the electronegative element

These rules are given in the order of importance. If, as is the case in CO, you must put the + charge on the electronegative element (oxygen) and the - charge on the more electropositive element (carbon) in order to maximize the number of covalent bonds, then so be it. Formal charges are calculated by comparing the number of valence electrons on an element (the group number in old-fashioned periodic charts) to the number of electrons that atom can claim in the compound. To assign ownership of an electron we count one electron in a shared pair, and both electrons in a lone pair, but to verify the Rule of 2 & 8 you count all of the electrons shared and lone pairs. (Is that confusing enough for you?)

A Standard Set of Functional Groups (FGs)

C & H

There are four functional groups that consist of only carbon and hydrogen: alkanes, alkenes, alkynes, and aromatic rings. These differ in terms of the oxidation state of carbon and they are the subject of most introductory chapters in textbooks. For the most part, the nomenclature of alkanes, alkenes and alkynes is logical, but at the start it is confusing because methane, ethane, propane and butane do not follow a pattern. To help with this you might use: "Me poor boy!" as a memory aid. The "M" is methane (or methyl) and "e" is ethane (or ethyl) and so forth. You might also notice that propane and pentane sound alike but mean different numbers of carbons. Be careful, these are easy to confuse.

C, H & O

With the addition of oxygen, the functional groups become relatively interesting. You will find that these can be classified by whether they have a carbonyl group or not. The carbonyl group has a double bond between carbon and oxygen. This significantly alters the reactivity of both atoms because of the inductive and resonance effects and the fact that each atom is an sp^2 hybrid atom. It is fun to take H, R, OH and OR and a carbonyl and work out all of the combinations and name them. That is essentially what was done in the first graphical abstract shown later in this primer.

C, H, O & N

Nitrogen rounds out the list of elements normally included in organic compounds and by using it along with oxygen carbon and hydrogen, the structures of all of the important functional groups can be obtained by remembering that organic chemistry is as simple as 1, 2, 3, and 4. Hydrogen (and halogens) – one bond. Oxygen – two. Nitrogen – three. Carbon – four. If one of these atoms has a different number of bonds, then it will have a charge or a bullet. You can count the number of electrons the atom can claim and find that charge as explained above.

A Standard Set of Transformations (T-goals)

There are some things that you just have to know. I insist that my students learn five ways to make primary alcohols because that is useful and easy. There are some three or four ways to make aldehydes that everybody else knows and you should learn. I suggest that you build a list of ways to make carbon-carbon bonds because, after all, making carbon-carbon bonds is what organic chemistry is all about anyway, isn't it? There are a limited number of ways to make three- and four-membered rings. Learn them. In short, here is a part of the 20% of "knowledge gained" that will give you a big return on any exam as "knowledge demonstrated." There are a number of transformations of this type, most are "name reactions." These reactions are so useful that the people who discovered them are famous. The Diels-Alder reaction is one of these. The Grignard synthesis of alcohols is another. One of the best places to find a list of name reactions is in the Merck Index, but the list is long and the pictures are not very good. Another place is in an advanced organic textbook. Included in this primer are two pages from Corey and Cheng's "The Logic of Chemical Synthesis." It shows how a real chemist views a name reaction: the product structure, the retron, the transformation, and the precursor. We will assume that this would work in general and try it in our synthesis if it looked like it would give the product we desire.

A Standard Set of Mechanistic Steps

When I tell my students that there are only sixteen things that I know, I am referring to the Standard Mechanistic steps listed in the table attached. This is a list I compiled to serve me when I run out of ideas. It is the "pocket-watch" mentality: You pull it out when you need it. My style is tends to be terse, packing as much information into as few words as possible, but for those of you who would like a more detailed treatment, I recommend Scudder's book: "Electron Flow in Organic Chemistry." His ideas and my own are similar. What is important here is that there are recognized standard steps which you can use without fear in your mechanisms. Later in this primer there will be an elaboration of the standard mechanistic steps themselves, but suffice it to say that they exist and that they are useful because they represent the culmination of formal analogies accumulated from a number of accepted mechanisms. How those mechanisms were determined is described in the next section heading. The important thing for you to recognize, as a student is which type of mechanism is it that you are studying.

If there are no conditions given and the reagents and products are neutral, then there is a good chance that the reaction is concerted. The same is true if heat (Δ) or light ($h\nu$) is on the arrow. If light is indicated, then there is a possibility that radicals are involved. (Look for ketones or halogens.) Radicals are also likely if peroxides are mentioned, or if AIBN is in the equation. Anions tend to have negatively charged intermediates either in the equation or on the arrow, and cations always have a Lewis acid somewhere at the start and a proton at the end. Once you see it, then it will become obvious unless it is a "trick question." Scudder gives a chart that is very useful for zwitterionic reactions. Since electrons flow from the source of electrons to the sink it is useful to be able to identify them. (See the chart.)

Standard Methods for Determining Mechanisms

The problem of actually figuring out how a reaction works is not easy. In fact, only a few reactions have been thoroughly studied because of this complexity, but over the years a standard approach has evolved. It consists of a series of steps that are easy to remember, if difficult to put into practice. The organic chemists who work on this are known by the name "physical organic" chemists, but it is often necessary for a synthetic organic chemist to don that cap in order to find out what is wrong with the reaction they are attempting.

TGT STRUCTURE	RETRON	TRANSFORM	PRECURSOR(S)
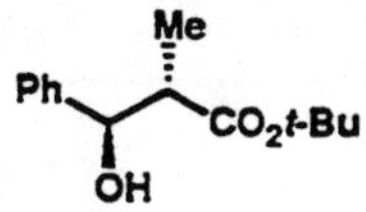	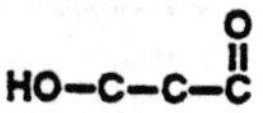	(E)-Enolate Aldol	PhCHO  + Me⟍CO₂t-Bu
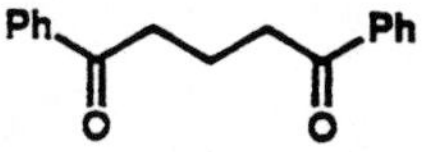	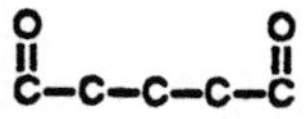	Michael	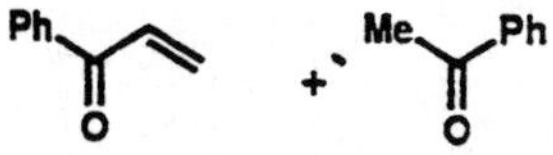
Et₃COH	EtCOH	Orgmet. Addn. to Ketone	Et₂CO + EtMet
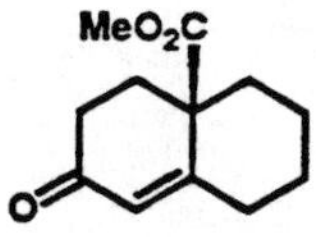	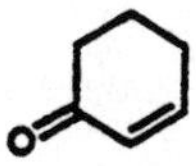	Robinson Annulation (Aldol + Michael)	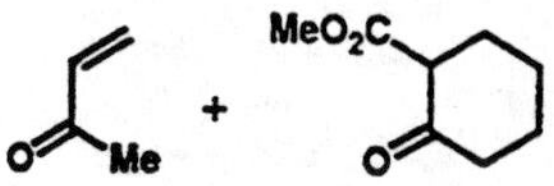
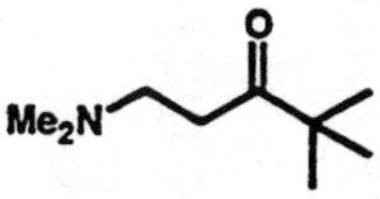	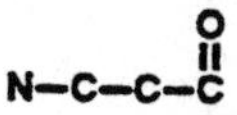	Mannich (Azaaldol)	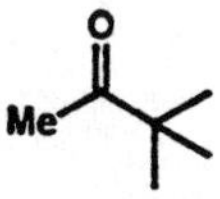 Me₂NH + CH₂O +
		Double Mannich	+ MeNH₂ +
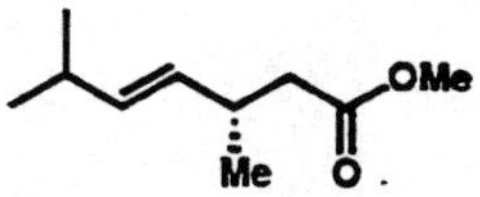		Claisen Rearrangement	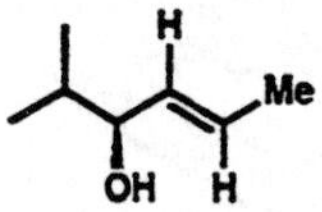 + MeCOX
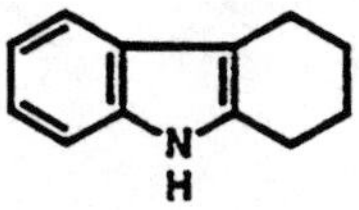	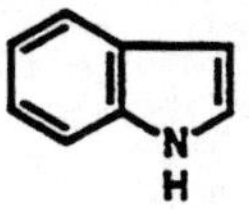	Fischer Indole	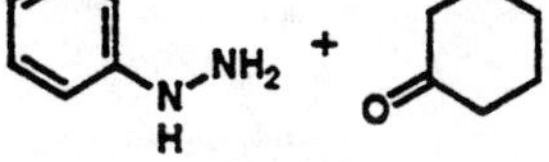
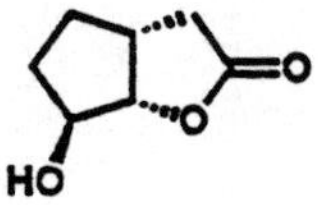	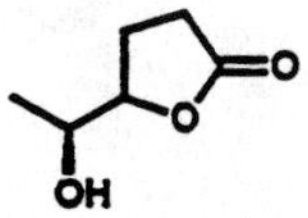	Oxy-lactonization of Olefin	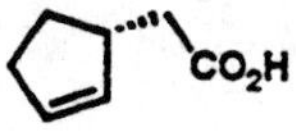

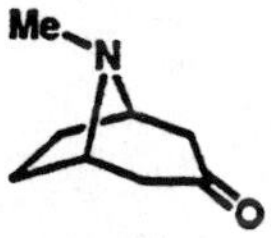

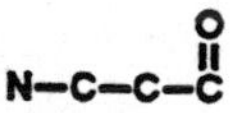

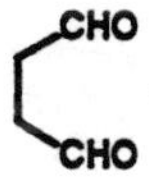

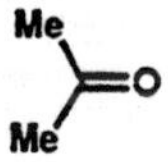

Chart 2. Disconnective Transforms

9

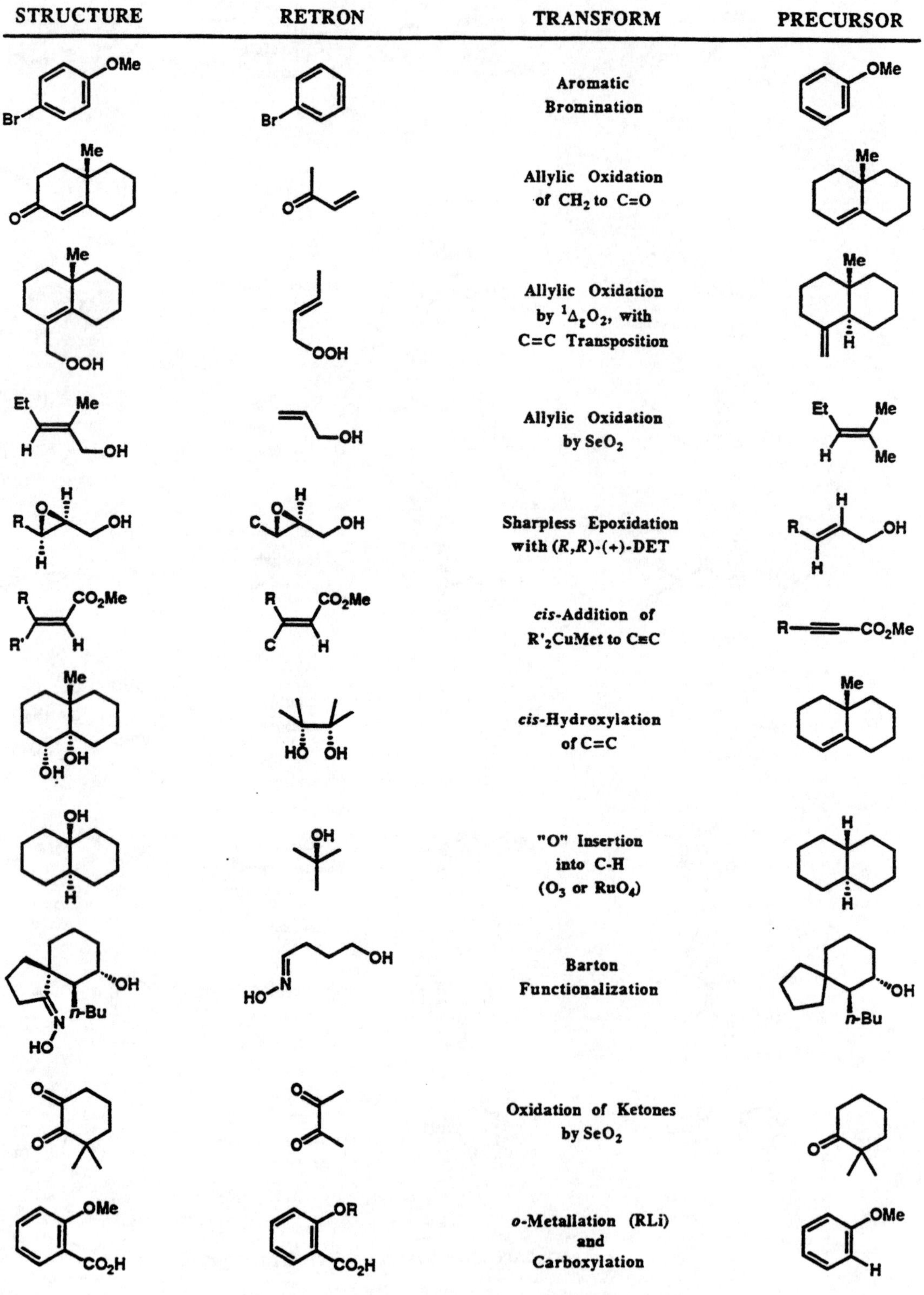

STRUCTURE	RETRON	TRANSFORM	PRECURSOR
		Aromatic Bromination	
		Allylic Oxidation of CH_2 to $C=O$	
		Allylic Oxidation by $^1\Delta_g O_2$, with $C=C$ Transposition	
		Allylic Oxidation by SeO_2	
		Sharpless Epoxidation with (R,R)-$(+)$-DET	
		cis-Addition of R'_2CuMet to $C\equiv C$	
		cis-Hydroxylation of $C=C$	
		"O" Insertion into C-H (O_3 or RuO_4)	
		Barton Functionalization	
		Oxidation of Ketones by SeO_2	
		o-Metallation (RLi) and Carboxylation	

Chart 3. Functional Group Removing Transforms

10

Tips for constructing a multi-step synthesis:

1. Work backward from the product toward the starting mateial. That way, the starting material for each single step synthesis becomes the product for the next single step. This idea is called retrosynthetic analysis, and it is such a good idea that they gave the guy who made it popular (E. J. Corey) the Nobel prize for it!

2. Figure out how many carbons need to be added. The easiest way to do this is to subtract the molecular formula of the starting material from the product. That way you will find out if water is lost or added, or if hydrogen (H_2) has been lost (oxidation), or added (reduction). Sometimes an obvious thing will turn up, like the addition of HOBr, etc

3. Identify the bonds that are broken and the bonds that are formed. We use curved arrows to indicate this process. It is the most important technique to master in the course. Bar none. If the bonds are carbon-carbon bonds, then the number of available techniques is limited: Grignard, S_N2 using cyanide or acetylide ions, Diels-Alder. Later, we will get more tools, but that is about all there are right now.

4. Identify changes in oxidation state that signal REDOX reactions. They are the only ones that don't require a mechanism, most of the time. I will never ask for a mechanism for the loss of water either. Sometimes it is obvious, and you can show it. There are a few other things, like hydrogenation, where the mechanism is not known.

5. Pay attention to the reaction conditions. If you call for an acid and a base in the same step it is trouble. Acids and bases react with each other. This is particularly troublesome if you want a Grignard reagent. The molecule cannot have any acidic hydrogens. The inductive effect indicates that hydrogen attached to an electronegative element will be acidic, and it is. So alcohols, amines, amide, and carboxylic acids, phenols are all bad.

6. Be aware of protecting groups like acetals and ketals. They do not change the oxidation state of the carbon, but they change its reactivity. Here is a case where you should know that acid and water takes the protecting group off. You can't use Zn (Hg) / HCl (conc) to reduce a ketone if another carbonyl is protected. (Here you would use W-K reduction.)

7. Be sensitive to the fact that regiochemistry is still important. Markovnikov's rule and Saytzeff's rules are still appropriate, and will continue to be important. Likewise, o,ρ directors influence regiochemistry.

8. Stereochemistry is important too. Words like cis and trans, erythro and threo are as common as dirt and in the mouths of students they feel the same. Likewise R and S, and E and Z get unfavorable reviews. The important thing here is to realize that a reaction involving an sp^2 carbon will give a racemic mixture. What that means is that you need to use the cartoon for a chiral center and either draw both enantiomers, or write "& enantiomer" to indicate that you know the other enantiomer exists. The same is true when making alkenes via elimination. Both diasteriomers form: cis and trans.

9. Three factors will drive all of organic chemistry in this course: The inductive effect (σ-system), the resonance effect (π-system), and the hybridization of the carbon and how it changes.

10. Remember the things you know. The test will have an emphasis on the chapters we just finished. Try to use something from those chapters first. If nothing is there then try using the old stuff. There are certain reactions that always give the same subunit (E. J. calls them "retrons"), watch for them.

11. Memorize the reactions on "Synthesis Paradiso" but while you are at it, learn how to use them and when. That chart is a kind of map that will guide you around through the functional groups we are studying. It is not exaustive, neither was it intended to be. You simply must be able to test out the water before you can swim. Synthesis Paradiso gives you that chance.

12. Above all, avoid drawing structures having five bonds to carbon. It freaks me out, totally. I cannot see another thing on the page until that mistake is fixed or marked wrong.

Stereochemistry, the arrangement of atoms in space is the most difficult aspect of organic chemistry and it has been so ever since its discovery in nature. Your challenges are two fold: (1) you must understand the arrangement in space, and (2) you must draw it so I can understand it too. (If I can't understand it, then it is automatically wrong. Remember that.)

Molecules that have flat (sp^2) regions such as alkenes and cations that can be attacked from either face. The atom attacked can be converted into a chiral (sp^3) center, if all four substituents are different. We will use R and S to designate the configuration, and we use dashes and wedges to draw it if the carbon is not in a 6-membered (cyclohexane) ring. Cyclohexane rings are important and we treat them with reverence. Never use the dash and wedge on them, draw the whole thing out. (Buy a template if you have to, they sell them at the bookstore. $12) Alkenes are made more complicated by the fact that there are two adjacent carbons involved. Both of them can be converted to chiral centers. When this happens in a cyclic compound the terms cis and trans apply, but if the molecule is acyclic (not cyclic) then we need different terms: erythro and threo. These terms are derived from the sugars named erythrose and threose (p. 418) In this course, the simple rule I teach is:

"syn addition to cis (or anti addition to trans) gives erythro"
"anti addition to cis (or syn addition to trans gives threo"

There are a long string of provisos needed to make this a real "rule" but for our limited palette of adducts and substrates, it works fine.

Syn Addition	Anti Addition	Stereo-random Addition
1. H_2 / cat (two H's add) (Markovnikov's rule does not apply.)	1. Br_2 / CCl_4, or any other inert solvent (two Br's add)	1. H^+, H_2O, hydration reaction (H and OH groups add Mark.)
2. $KMnO_4$ (two OH groups add) (Markovnikov's rule does not apply.)	2. Br_2 / H_2O, a reactive solvent (Br and OH groups add Markovnikov)	2. HX, X is Cl, Br, I, or OSO_3H, etc. (H and X groups add Mark.)
3. (1) BH_3; H_2O_2, HO^- (H & OH groups add, anti-Markovnikov)	3. Br_2 / ROH, any alcohol (Br and OR groups add Markovnikov)	3. HBr / benzoyl peroxide, or others (H and X groups add anti-Mark.)
4. Diels-Alder (diene unit adds)	Br^+ always adds to the carbon attached to the most H's like H^+ would have.	H^+ always adds to the carbon attached to the most H's

The question is how are these verbal rules converted to pictures that are acceptable? Our palette of alkenes includes tetrasub'd, trisub'd, disub'd and monosub'd. The regiochemistry is dictated by Markovnikov's rule only in cases where the alkene is unsymmetrical (different on each carbon), and so are the substituents (different on each carbon) added during the reaction.

Let us agree to draw the alkene on the Butcher's "butterfly" structure, and to draw the adduct with the substituents drawn in the plane of the alkene carbons to emphasize the syn or anti stereochemistry of the addition. Consistency is everything at this point. Put the two substituents on the bottom side of the "butterfly" on the wedges and the substituents on the top on the dashed lines. That always does it for me. Make sure you can assign R and S to the carbons in the structure.

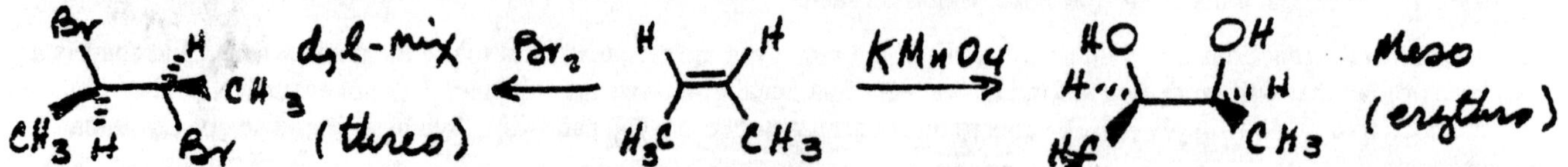

*** Secret information: Achiral starting materials do not rotate the plane of polarized light. Reactions with achiral starting materials yield products as a d,l-mixture (enantiomers present in equal amounts) or meso (a molecule that is its own mirror image). In either case, the product will not rotate the plane of polarized light if the starting material did not.

***Sensitive information: Chiral starting materials undergoing an S_N2 reaction will undergo inversion of configuration. That means if the starting material rotated the plane of polarized light, the product will also. You cannot predict the direction the light will rotate, but you can assign R and S to both starting material and product.

"Pop Quiz"   *Your name:*_____

1. (a) What "cartoon" (or basis for a correct structure) would you draw for an alkene <u>*every time*</u> in
     Butcher's class? Draw it here.

   (b) Would you ever "forget" to draw that cartoon on an exam, or any other document of importance? __NO__

2. Consider this exam problem concerning alkene addition:

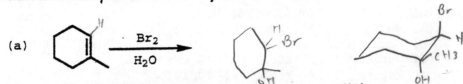

   (a) Can Markovnikov's rule be applied to this problem? ___Yes___
   (b) What are the two groups that will add to the double bond? ___OH Br___
   (c) Which one of those groups will add to the carbon in the double bond that is already attached to the
       methyl group? ___OH___
   (d) Will the two groups add to the same side, or opposite sides, of the double bond? ___opposite___
   (e) Is the product a molecule containing a cyclohexane (6-carbon) ring? ___yes___
   (f) Will the product structure require dashes and wedges on the new sp^3 carbons? In other words, do the
       new additions make the number of different substituents equal four, and are they contained in a
       6-membered ring, or not? ___NO___
   (g) Draw the structure of the product that conforms to all of the answers you gave above.
   (h) If the substituents added from the other sides, would the same product form? If not, then there are
       two products to draw. Draw the second one also.

3. Now that you know what I wanted, do the same for the rest of these questions.

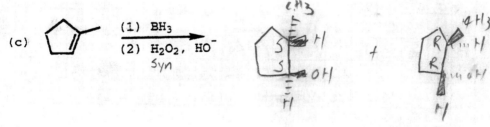

Standard Mechanistic Sets
(June 1985)

PREMISE: With the exception of oxidations, all organic reactions can be explained using one or more of the mechanistic steps listed below:

1. *Concerted:* A reactions in which

$$\Sigma \ (4q+2)_s + (4r)_a \ \text{components} \neq 2n$$

is Δ allowed, otherwise, it is $h\nu$ allowed.
Here q, r, and n are integers.
(Summary of the Woodward-Hoffmann Rules)

2. *Anions:* (a) Act as a base (removes H^+)
   (b) Nucleophilic attack on R-X (S_N2)
   (c) Nucleophilic attack on carbonyls (1,2 addition)
   (d) Nucleophilic attack on α,β unsaturated ketones (1,4 or Michael addition)
   (e) SET (entry into the radical mechanistic set)

3. *Cations:* (a) Act as an acid (loses H^+)
   (b) 1,2 shifts of H^- and R^- (Δ allowed, W-H)
   (c) Electrophilic attack on π-bonds in double bonds and aromatic rings (Friedel-Crafts)
   (d) Electrophilic attack on σ-bonds and ω-orbitals containing e^- pairs
   (e) SET (entry into the radical mechanistic set)

4. *Radical:* (a) H• abstraction (takes the entire atom)
   (b) Coupling
   (c) Addition to π-bonds in double bonds and aromatic rings
   (d) Disproportionation
   (e) Electron and/or halogen atom abstraction

PROVISO: Please note that each step given above can be used in the reverse sense (e.g., coupling as retro-homolytic cleavage). Furthermore, topological equivalents and analogy must often be used.

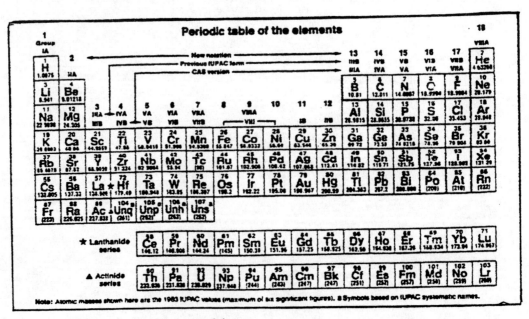

FLOW CHARTS FOR THE CLASSIFICATION OF ELECTRON SOURCES AND SINKS

For some individuals, a graphical presentation of a process in the form of a flow chart greatly helps them understand and visualize the overall process (Figure A.1).

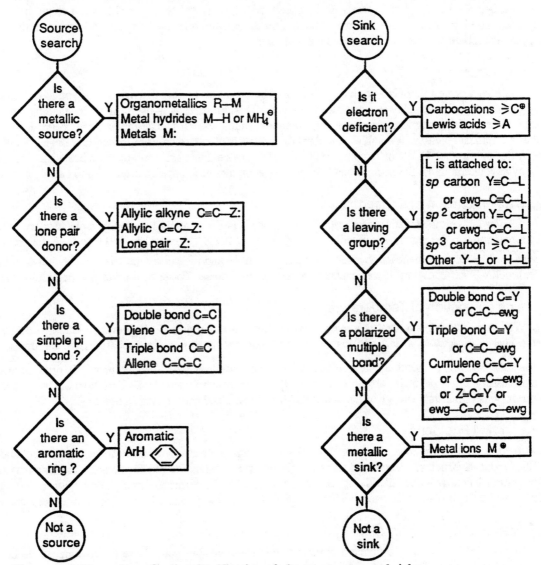

Figure A.1 Flow charts for the classification of electron sources and sinks.

Products

It is impossible to know what you are dealing with until you know what the products are and the ratios in which they are produced. In ages past, this was done without the aid of modern instrumentation by using melting point and elemental analysis. These are still used, but a variety of chromatography and spectroscopic techniques have been added to the arsenal. This statement explains two things that are of value: (1) You will be asked to learn about the historical methods, meaning derivatives of aldehydes and ketones, because that used to be really useful once; and, (2) You will be required to learn about the spectroscopic techniques that replaced the older methods. No matter how difficult those techniques may appear, the problems they present are very much easier than the problems our antecedents faced without them!

Thermodynamics

Believe it or not, there is a book by J. Benson that has tables of data that will allow you to calculate the heat content and entropy of formation for virtually any organic compound. This information is useful in understanding why a molecule forms. In the years before mechanistic organic chemistry, thermodynamics was all that a chemist had to go on by way of predicting the course of a chemical reaction. A notable example is the synthesis of isooctane from isobutylene during W.W.II. It made it possible for the Allies to win the "Battle of Britain." Still, the chemists couldn't agree about the mechanism until long after the war was over. Anyway, thermodynamics is important, and modern computer programs are often used to calculate those quantities.

Kinetics as a Function of Concentration

The order, or molecularity, of a reaction is important in determining how many molecules are involved in the transition state of a reaction. In the reactions you will study, this number is the "1" or "2" in S_N1 and S_N2, for example. These quantities are determined by running the reaction at different concentrations and measuring the change that causes in the rate of the reaction. Your textbook will explain more, if it is important to passing the course. For now, it is simply fun to know how it is done, right?

Kinetics as a Function of Temperature

There are two ways to treat the kinetic data obtained as a function of temperature. One is the Arrhenius equation which gives the energy of activation (E_a) and log A. It turns out that the log A term measures the entropy change on going to the transition state, and this is useful in determining whether a concerted reaction is taking place. In order to bring this quantity ($\Delta S^{\neq}$) out it is necessary to use Erying's "absolute rate theory" to analyze the kinetic data. Your textbook will have a section in it on that topic, but for this primer it is enough to know that the theory exists and can be used in this way.

The Hammond Postulate

It turns out that the transition state is a nice idea rather than a chemical that can be bottled and studied. For years, many speculated about its structure. Hammond was the only one brave enough to put his name to the idea that an exothermic reaction had a transition state that looked like the starting material, and that the transition state in an endothermic reaction looked liked the product. This idea is well-liked and accepted to a great extent. It simply makes it easier to think about a transition state that way.

Linear Free Energy Relationships

It may not be possible to detect a transition-state structure, but many have tried. One of the best ways is to see how substituents alter the rate of a reaction. Making the starting material electron rich and comparing its rate of reaction to a molecule having either no enhancement or one that was electron deficient seemed like a good idea. It turned out well, and that is now a standard treatment that is done to study a reaction mechanism.

Detection of Reactive Intermediates

Reactive intermediates, like radicals, are transient. That means that their concentration never builds up to a significant level. They can sometimes be detected even when their concentration is very low. You can imagine how difficult that is, and how much cleverness has been expended on this problem. The results are worthwhile, and you reap the benefit even if you don't know how the work was done, you can still have confidence in the textbook. One of the activities that you participate in when you write a mechanism, is to speculate about reactions and intermediates. Your conjecture is a hypothesis. Take time to think how much fun it might be to find the intermediate that proves your mechanism is right, and discover you are a chemist.

16

3. Paradigms are working models that can be used to solve problems

The Scientific Method

Codified Common Sense

"Why do you teach the Scientific Method and never give us a reason to use it?" This is a common complaint. The answer is almost humorous: We expect students to use the Scientific Method for everything. The Scientific Method is a common-sense approach to solving problems when you cannot think of anything else. Consider the following cryptogram of a common phrase: AV LYY PZ OBTHU. How would you solve a puzzle like this one? Use the Scientific Method. It consists of six steps: (1)Reading the literature (You would find that a cryptogram is a word puzzle in which each letter substitutes for a letter in the phrase),   (2) Making an observation (One of the words has three letters and a double letter.), (3) Formulating a hypothesis (Suppose the word is ALL.), (3) Trying it in an experiment (BE ALL TO QUIPS. Hum, maybe ALL isn't the right word….), (5) Cycling through those steps repeatedly until you have confidence in the answer (I will leave that to you.), and then (6) Publishing the result. In the scientific community, others will read the publication, formulate a new hypothesis and the process repeats until the observations and hypotheses are so far removed from the common experience that science takes on an aura of mystery that is not deserved. This process is also responsible for the abstract nature of the Art found in organic chemistry, and it is the reason why my mother doesn't understand what I do.

Application to Spectra

In most areas of study, memorization of facts and concepts will suffice, but in organic chemistry, the place where the Scientific Method works the best is in the interpretation of spectra. Here, just like the word game given above, all that you need to know is given, but in order to start you have to guess. The Inductive Effect, Resonance Effect, Changes with Hybridization, and Effect of neighboring groups will provide the basis for the guesses, but they are still guesses. At the first inconsistency, the old hypothesis has to be discarded and replaced with a new one. A scientist who "bends the nail until he hits it on the head" is dangerous to the profession. This is called "advocacy research." Avoid it. The closer you come to believing your results, the more suspicious you should become.

Open-Mindedness

If there were a single thing that I could teach you it would be that open-mindedness is the secret to good science. Open-mindedness is the basis for hope and understanding in everything from personal relationships to cultural understanding and world peace. In a scientific discipline, this means reading everything whether it relates to your field of study or not. Don't forget: Introduction of new paradigms is an identified method of creativity. So read everything – forget nothing. If you find something that interests you, then you will find a way to apply it to your field of interest.

4. Creation of Art is the purpose of life

"Who am I? Why am I alive? Where am I going?" – common questions through the ages (During the Viet Nam war, I saw a card with the answers: Who am I? (A face among the masses.) Why am I alive? (To pay taxes.) Where am I going? (Into the armed services.)). These questions are frequent subjects in humanities courses, what do they have to do with chemistry? Science is dedicated to the relentless pursuit of physical truths and the Scientific Method only works when it is applied with an open mind that is unbiased by emotion, or practically anything else. The truth should be made available to everyone through the free exchange of ideas and information because physical truths are true for everyone. What an individual can contribute is creativity: Like using plastic bags filled with water to build dams against the flood, creativity is a process that takes something that is available to everyone and creates a work of Art. The definition of what constitutes Art is beyond the scope of this primer, but I tend to be liberal in my interpretation of the term. I believe that through the creation of Art, human beings imitate God and that this is the purpose of life. Chemistry is an Art form that has reached that level of abstraction that can only be appreciated by the practitioners. Make it your Art form and enjoy life in its full measure. Who am I? (A chemist.) Why am I alive? (To create a work of Art.) Where am I going? (Back to the lab as soon as possible.)

Using Both Sides of Your Brain

Art School, Drawing Lessons, and Working from Models

Drawing What You Need to Show

Chemists are lazy (You heard it from me.), they only draw what they need to and "leave the obvious vague." (van Gogh) So, when you get ready to draw something decide what is important and emphasize that and abbreviate the rest. An aromatic ring is the best example. If the ring is the same from start to finish you can draw a circle in the center of the hexagon. If you are attacking the ring, or you need to show resonance in that ring, drew the bonds in. There are levels of detail. If the question is about the electron dot structures, draw all the dots. If the question is about lone-pairs, draw them. If the question is about the functional group, leave out the lone pairs. A mechanism that has multiple steps will require multiple intermediates. Don't pile a lot of curved arrows on one structure. Even if you know the answer, that will get marked wrong because that is not the way it is done. Check out the essay on power, above. In a synthesis, draw out the structures when C-C bonds are made. If you have a series of functional group interconversions (FGIs) you can stack the reagents, but not when C-C bonds are introduced.

Showing What You Need to Know

There are two types of structural information that have to be drawn: Regiochemistry and Stereochemistry. Regiochemistry follows Markovnikov's rule for the addition to alkenes, and it follows the path directed by the first substituent in electrophilic aromatic substitution reactions. It is difficult to miss unless you forget to put it in. Stereochemistry is another problem. Every time you draw a carbon having four different substituents attached to it, you need to make some mention of the fact. The easiest way I have found is to draw the carbon by using dashes & wedges, and then noting in the margin that this is one of a pair of enantiomers or diasteriomers, as appropriate. There are few other accepted ways. (I always write & enantiomer rather than + enantiomer, because + enantiomer means the one that rotates the plane of light to the right while "&" and "and" mean and.) Dashes and wedges do not belong on six-membered rings because there is an accepted way of drawing them: You can't tell whether the substituents are axial or equatorial. If you try to improve on the accepted drawing it will probably be marked wrong, so use the right structure.

Dashes and wedges only belong on sp^3 hybrid carbons. Some people and some textbooks try to use them on sp^2 carbons once in a while, but I always mark that wrong. It is also wrong to omit the stereochemistry from double bonds. They can be cis or trans if you can see hydrogens on the same side or opposite, respectively. They can be E or Z, when hydrogens don't give the signal. Placing dashes and wedges on alkenes is like "guilding the lily." Properly drawn, all of the information is packed in the "butterfly" structure and it does not need to be improved. There are cases where it is necessary to leave a note saying that both diasteriomers form. (I would use "& diasteriomer" for that.)

Seeing What You Need to Draw – Drawing What You See

Drawing complex, 3-dimensional structure is challenging for student and professor alike. Be compassionate when your teacher draws on the board. It is a tough job and it is hard to see when you stand too close to your work the way we do. Still, the best way I know of to practice drawing is to make a model of what you want to draw, hold it up to the board, close one eye and draw exactly what you see on the board behind the model. Try it. It is Leonardo Da Vinci's method, and it works.

Natural and Unnatural Products

Now here is an amusing concept. There are a variety of organic compounds isolated each year from natural sources: plants and animals. These frequently prove to have useful properties, some have interesting structures, others have both. These are natural products, and the synthesis of natural products is a branch of organic chemistry closely related to multi-step synthesis. Chemists are at a disadvantage in competing with nature, so it is frequently necessary to protect one functional group while modifying another. Consequently, the synthesis of a natural products proceeds through a series of unnatural products until the very last one. Chemists sometimes prepare unnatural products intentionally. Often this is done to test a hypothesis, but sometimes the unnatural product has some value, either intellectual or monetary. Occasionally the goal is to rid the environment of some nuisance or pollutant. The future will present a series of challenges, some resulting from discoveries yet to be made, others from expedient decisions made in the past. It will take an informed electorate as well as teams of scientists to make the decisions that need to be made. If education is slighted, then life, itself, will become unnatural. Stay in school. Learn your chemistry! Vote.

Drug Structures

Fun with Functional Groups
(This is not a test. It is not homework. It will not hurt you. It is just fun.)

Hidden Pictures -- Can you find...
(a) the functional groups. Circle each one and name it.
(b) the chiral centers (carbons having four different groups attached). Star (*) them.
(c) the protons that can participate in H-bonding. Underline them.
(d) the missing electron pairs. Draw them in.

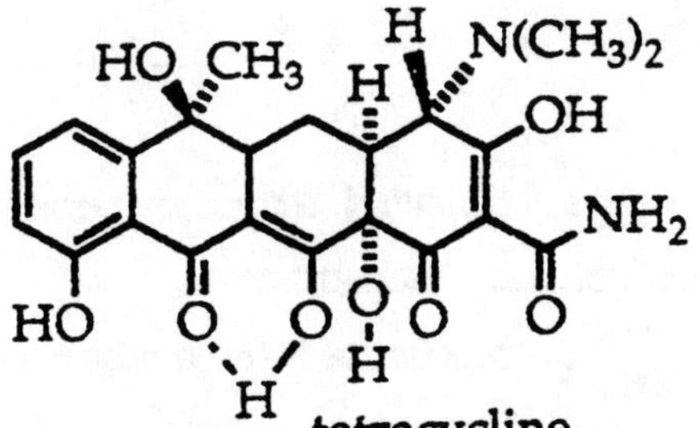

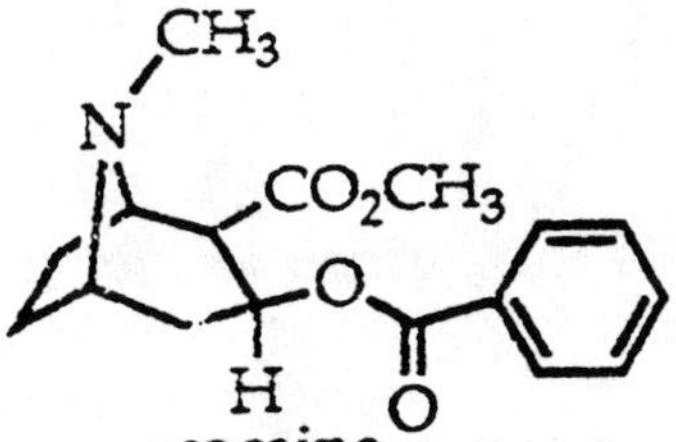

cocaine

tetracycline

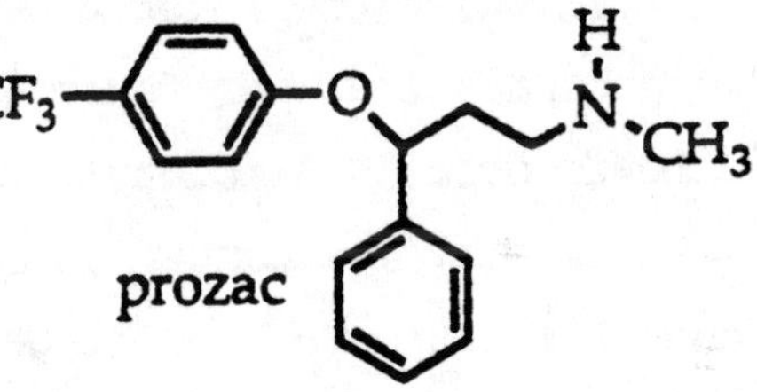

prozac

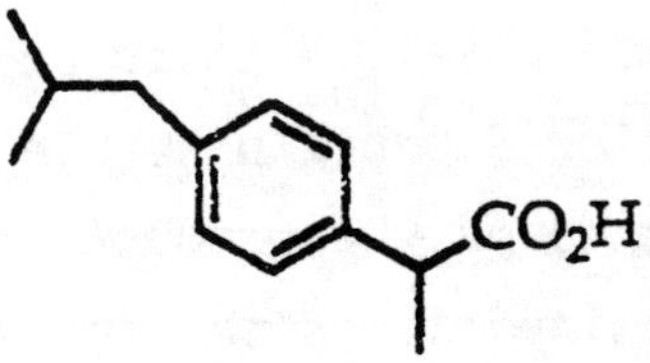

advil, ibuprofin, or nuprin – all

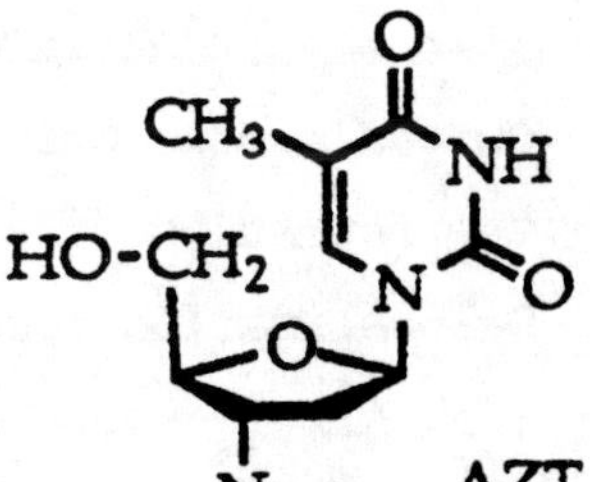

RU 486

AZT

(Compare to the structure
for 2'-deoxythymidine 5'-
phosphate)

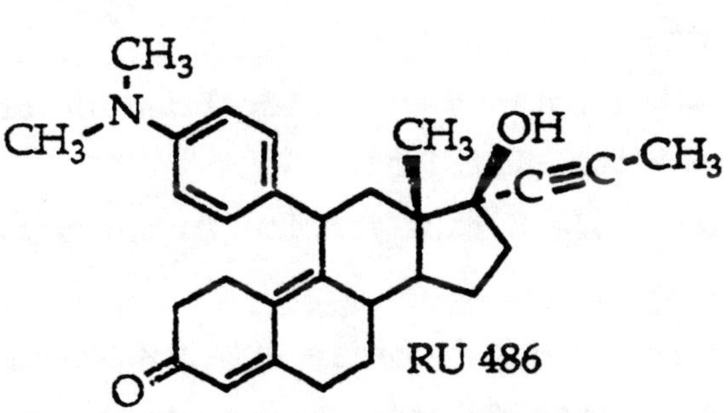

Forbidden Things

A list of forbidden things:

- five bonds to carbon
- ten electrons around any first row element
- naked carbons (the symbol "C" surrounded by nothing)
- sticks used to represent hydrogens (a stick represents a bond to carbon)
- 1° cations (these never form - don't draw them.)
- anti-aromatic compounds (planar compounds having 0,4,8,... π-electrons.)
- acyl anions (The acyl cation and radical are ok, the anion is not.)

Notes:

- 1° means the head atom is bonded to one carbon (the exception is methyl)
- Electron dot structures:
    1. Maximize the number of covalent bonds
       This is especially important if it gives all atoms an octet.
    2. Minimize the charge separation.
    3. Place the negative charge on the electronegative element.
    Poor structures are ones without an octet on each atom, and the order in which the rules are given above is the order in which they should be applied. No fewer than 6 electrons nor more than 8.
- A Lewis acid is a molecule that acts as if it were a proton. In general it will have at its center an atom having only six electrons. It needs eight to complete its octet and it gets it from some Lewis base. A Lewis acid acts on on a neutral molecule to generate another Lewis acid until a stable salt results.
- Anti-Markovnikov is a term denoting the appearance of the product and not the mode of addition, thus when a 1° alcohol is obtained it is the anti-Markovnikov result, because addition of water never goes that way.
- F-C alkylation gives 2° and 3° substituents attached to aromatic rings. To get 1° one must acylate and reduce.
- Curved arrows point toward the planned movement of electrons and prevent the formation of five bonds to carbon, etc...
- Delocalization spells disaster
    1. Alkyl groups stabilize alkyl cations via delocalization of charge in the σ system, which is not too efficient.
    2. Allyl stabilizes the charge via delocalization in the π system. It is more efficient.
    3. The arenium ion formed when an electrophile attacks an aromatic ring will combine allylic and 3° type delocalization where possible. That is how to explain o and p directing groups.

Helpful Hints

There are a number of helpful suggestions for taking exams that have surfaced over the years. Here is a partial list of things that are guaranteed to keep you from scoring an exam because they will blow your credibility every time they turn up: five bonds to carbon; ten electrons around any first row element; naked carbons (the symbol "C" surrounded by nothing); a primary cation (1° cations never form in solution – don't draw them!); anti-aromatic compounds (any planar compound having 0, 4, 8, ... π-electrons); acyl anions (acyl cations and acyl radicals are ok, but the acyl anion is not). Before turning in any paper in check everything you have written to make sure doesn't have one of these in it. Leave some time for checking at the end of the hour.

The Parable of the 5-Legged Dog

When my daughter was little, we used to draw pictures of dogs. You can draw pictures of dogs having four legs, and dogs having three legs. If you catch them from the right angle, even a two-legged dog looks ok. It simply has the legs on one side of its body in front of the ones on the other side so you can't see them. But, if you draw a five-legged dog, my daughter would think it was stupid, and she would probably think you were stupid.

Carbon is very much like the dog in the discussion above. It normally has four bonds. A carbon having three bonds will have either a charge (+ or -) or a bullet (•) indicating that it is a free radical. Even a carbon having two bonds is possible. This represents a very reactive carbon and it is called a carbene. The topic is advanced, but fascinating. Find out about it before you leave the organic. (Carbenes are really interesting.) But, if you draw five bonds to carbon and I see it, I cannot see anything else on the page until that error is corrected or marked wrong.

Now if you pay attention to the change in hybridization, you will be ok. A carbon having four bonds will be tetrahedral (sp^3) while one having three bonds could be either sp^3 or sp^2, but there is no hybridization for a carbon having five bonds because 10 electrons around carbon is too many. Every atom in the first row is too small for 10 electrons, so be careful with your dots, too. Having 10 electrons around oxygen or nitrogen is just as bad as it is on carbon.

Study Habits ("Learn for Life" – "Learn to Survive")

The Holiness of Minute Particulars

"Labour well the Minute Particulars, attend to the Little Ones....
He would do good to another must do it in Minute Particulars
General Good is the plea of the scoundrel, hypocrite & flatterer
For Art & Science cannot exist but in minutely organized Particulars"
(William Blake, "Jerusalem")

Organic chemistry may be unique in terms of the amount of attention to detail that it requires. It is so hard to explain that one must be so careful, because even slight omissions can cause major errors. Details are the key. Pay attention. Be careful.

The 80/20 rule:

Everyone's talking about the 80:20 rule, according to which 80% of the credit is given for 20% of the knowledge. So where is that 20%? It is the fraction of your effort devoted to mastering the language of the discipline. No kidding! Eighty percent of your credit on an exam comes from mastering the way we write and draw and use the language: terms and definitions, mechanisms, synthesis and chemical structures. Learn how to use them and make an A. The frustrating part of this is the 60% you don't get tested on in class. I think it is important to keep in mind that these tests are comprehensive, but they are not exhaustive. What that means is that even material you are not tested over is as important as the material you are tested on. Frequently, a student will study old exams and know all of that material and complain that they studied the wrong material. The problem is that there is plenty of material and it is unlikely that any two tests will contain the same questions even if the same person makes out both exams. The same problem turns up when studying for the final. Study the material – leave the testing to your teacher.

Functional Groups

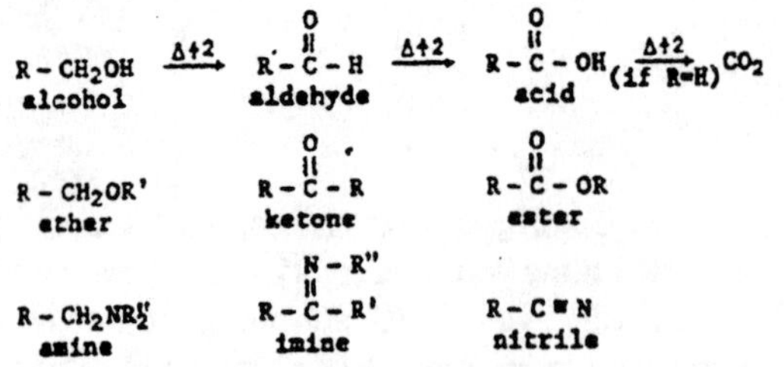

$R-CH_2OH$ alcohol $\xrightarrow{\Delta+2}$ $R-\overset{\overset{O}{\|}}{C}-H$ aldehyde $\xrightarrow{\Delta+2}$ $R-\overset{\overset{O}{\|}}{C}-OH$ acid $\xrightarrow{\Delta+2}$ (if R=H) CO_2

$R-CH_2OR'$ ether $R-\overset{\overset{O}{\|}}{C}-R$ ketone $R-\overset{\overset{O}{\|}}{C}-OR$ ester

$R-CH_2NR''_2$ amine $R-\overset{\overset{N-R''}{\|}}{C}-R'$ imine $R-C\equiv N$ nitrile

Oxidation state changes by 2 column to column.

Hydrogen bonding:

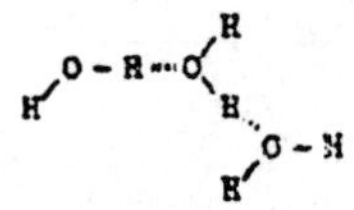

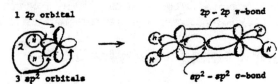

Lewis base - "Have pair, will share."
Lewis acid - "Need two from you."

Line Structures

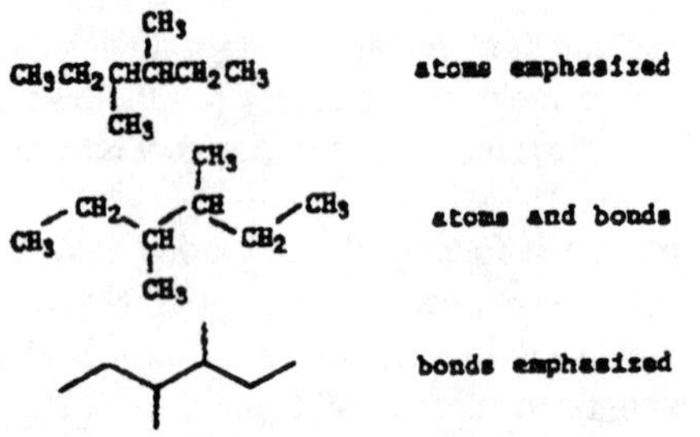

$CH_3CH_2\overset{\overset{CH_3}{|}}{\underset{\underset{CH_3}{|}}{CH}}CHCH_2CH_3$ atoms emphasized

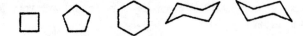 atoms and bonds

  bonds emphasized

R· Chain Mechanisms

Initiation: $|\overline{Cl}-\overline{Cl}| \xrightarrow{h\nu} 2|\overline{Cl}\cdot$

Propagation:
$|\overline{Cl}\cdot + CH_4 \xrightarrow{H\cdot abs.} HCl + \dot{C}H_3$
$CH_3\cdot + |\overline{Cl}-\overline{Cl}| \longrightarrow CH_3-\overline{Cl}| + |\overline{Cl}\cdot$

Termination: $CH_3\cdot + |\overline{Cl}\cdot \longrightarrow CH_3\overline{Cl}|$

Cyclic Structures - Chairs and Boats and Planes

all axial   all   all equatorial

Notice parallel lines in the ring and to substituents.

Orbitals and Hybridization

1 2p orbital

2

3 sp² orbitals

2p - 2p π-bond

sp² - sp² σ-bond

Alkenes - Addition and Elimination

Trans addition

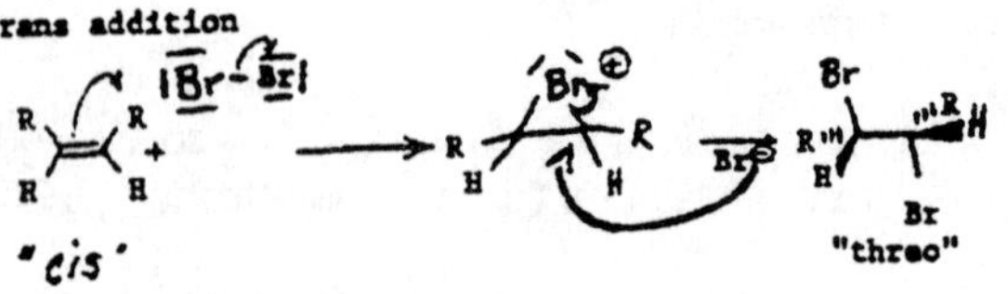

"cis"   "threo"

Elimination

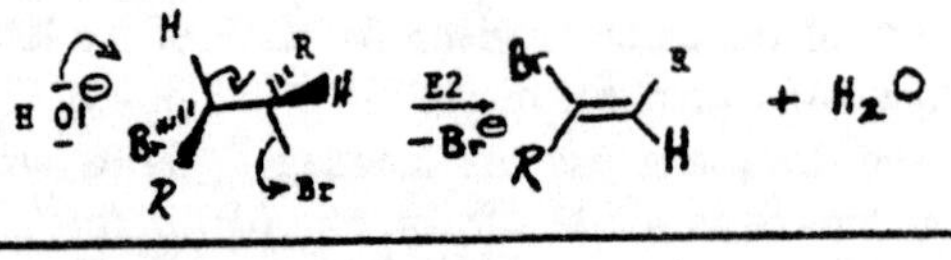

$\xrightarrow[-Br]{E2}$ $+ H_2O$

Borane and Anti-Markovnikov Addn.

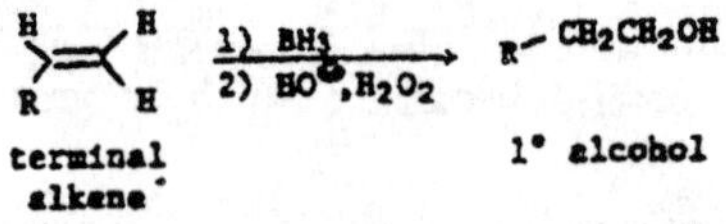

$\begin{array}{c} \overset{H}{\underset{H}{}} = \overset{H}{\underset{H}{}} \end{array}$ $\xrightarrow[2) HO^{\ominus}, H_2O_2]{1) BH_3}$ $R-CH_2CH_2OH$

terminal alkene   1° alcohol

(This is really important. Learn it!)

Glycolization and Ozonolysis

Glycolization breaks the π-bond

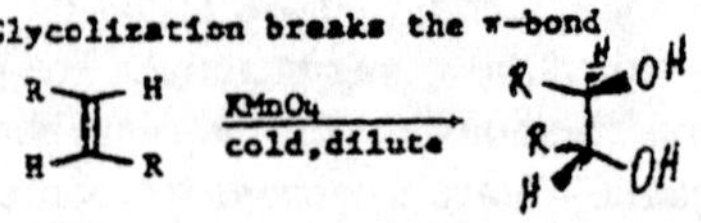

$\xrightarrow[\text{cold,dilute}]{KMnO_4}$ cis addition to the double bond

Ozonolysis breaks both σ and π bonds

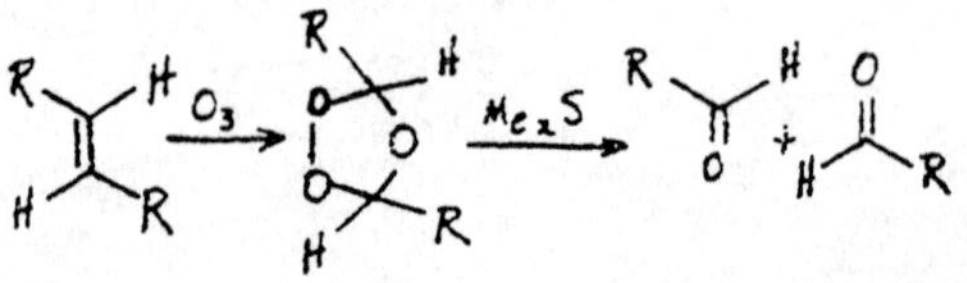

$\xrightarrow{O_3}$ $\xrightarrow{Me_2S}$

Molecular Orbitals - spⁿ Hybrids

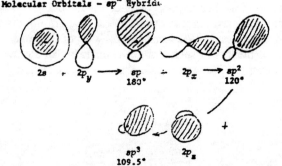

2s + 2p_y → sp 180° ÷ 2p_x → sp² 120°

sp³ 109.5°   2p_z   +

Conjugation – MO Theory vs. Resonance

VB Theory
Resonance
(no atoms move)

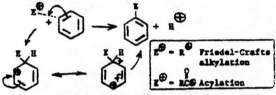

MO Theory

2 nodes	ϕ_3 —
1 node	ϕ_2 — LUMO
no nodes	ϕ_1 ⥮ HOMO

Benzene – Kekulé and Hückels' Numbers

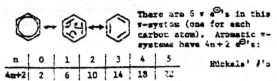

There are 6 π e$^{\ominus}$'s in this π-system (one for each carbon atom). Aromatic π-systems have $4n+2$ e$^{\ominus}$'s:

n	0	1	2	3	4	5
$4n+2$	2	6	10	14	18	22

Hückels' #'s

Electrophilic Aromatic Substitution

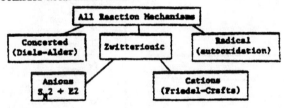

E$^{\oplus}$ = R$^{\oplus}$ Friedel-Crafts alkylation

E$^{\oplus}$ = RC$\overset{O}{\oplus}$ Acylation

Double bonds drawn in the benzene ring for emphasis.

Activating Groups (o,p directors)

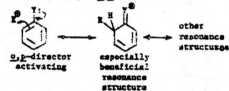

o,p-director activating ⟷ especially beneficial resonance structure ⟷ other resonance structures

−Y = −ÑR$_2$, −ÖR, ⬡ , or −R   {halogens deactivate the ring}

Standard Mechanistic Sets

All Reaction Mechanisms

Concerted (Diels-Alder)   Zwitterionic   Radical (autooxidation)

Anions S$_N$2 + E2   Cations (Friedel-Crafts)

Chiral Molecules

These four structures represent one molecule:

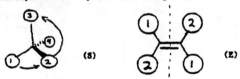

D-glyceraldehyde (R)

Priority Rules (R and S, E and Z)

1. Higher At.No. – higher priority
2. First point of difference is used
3. Multiple bonds duplicate the single bond scheme

(S)   (E)

Diastereomers

CO$_2$H	CO$_2$H	CO$_2$H
HO—H	H—OH	H—OH
H—OH	HO—H	H—OH
CO$_2$H	CO$_2$H	CO$_2$H

d,l mixture (racemic)   meso (inactive)

S$_N$2 – Primary Alkyl Halides

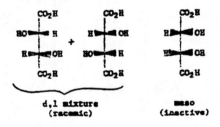

Nucleophilic attack

S$_N$2 always means inversion of configuration

Unimolecular S$_N$1

vacant p orbital

$CH_3-C\overset{CH_3}{\underset{CH_3}{-}}CH_3 \quad -|Cl|^{\ominus} \quad CH_3-\overset{CH_3}{C}CH_3 \quad :Nu \quad CH_3-C-Nu$

3° cation > 2° cation
(1° cations do not exist in nature)

23

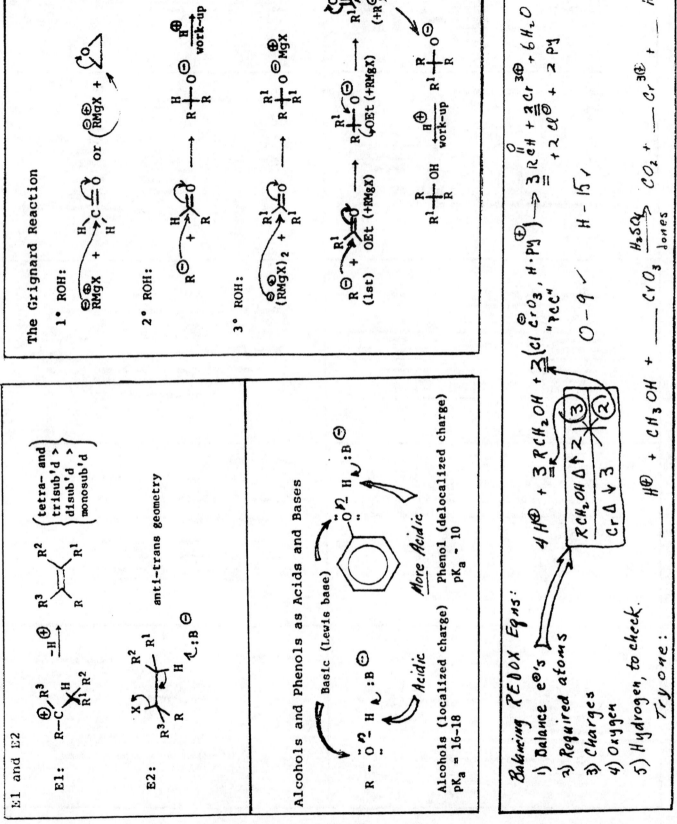

The Grignard Reaction

1° ROH:

or RMgX +

work-up

2° ROH:

work-up

3° ROH:

(RMgX)₂ +

(1st) OEt (+RMgX)

OEt (+RMgX)

(+R, MgX)

work-up

E1 and E2

E1:

$$R-C \overset{\oplus}{} R^3 \xrightarrow{-H^\oplus}$$

⎱ tetra– and
⎰ trisub'd >
⎱ disub'd >
⎰ monosub'd

E2:

anti–trans geometry

Alcohols and Phenols as Acids and Bases

Basic (Lewis base)

More Acidic

Acidic

$R - \overset{..}{\underset{..}{O}} - H$:B⊖

Phenol (delocalized charge)
$pK_a \sim 10$

Alcohols (localized charge)
$pK_a = 16–18$

Balancing REDOX Eqns:
1) Balance e⊖'s
2) Required atoms
3) Charges
4) Oxygen
5) Hydrogen, to check.

Try one:

$$4H^\oplus + 3 \underset{R}{RCH_2OH} + 2(Cl \overset{\ominus}{CrO_3}, H \cdot Py^\oplus) \longrightarrow 3 \overset{O}{RCH} + 2\underset{=}{Cr}^{3\oplus} + 6H_2O$$
"PCC"
$+ 2 Cl^\ominus + 2 Py$

O – 9 ✓   H – 15 ✓

$RCH_2OH \ \Delta \uparrow 2$
$Cr \ \Delta \downarrow 3$

③
②

$$\_\_ H^\oplus + CH_3OH + \_\_ CrO_3 \xrightarrow[dones]{H_2SO_4} \_\_ CO_2 + \_\_ Cr^{3\oplus} + \_\_ H_2O$$

Annotated Graphical Abstracts

Functional Groups

The important thing here is that an organic chemist treats functional groups the way other chemists treat elements. "R" in these pictures represents the rest of the molecule but the hybridization of the carbon attached is sp3. If the carbon is in an aromatic ring, an organic chemist will use the abbreviation "Ar," with apologies to argon.

Lewis Electron-Dot Structures and Hydrogen Bonding

Electron-dot structures use dots for individual electrons or lines for pairs of electrons. Lone pairs of electrons are available to be shared with a Lewis acid. A Lewis acid is a molecule like BF_3 that needs a pair of electrons (it needs 2 electrons) to finish its octet. Hydrogen bonding is possible if a hydrogen is attached to an electronegative element like oxygen or nitrogen. Here, the proton has a partial positive ($\delta +$) that is attracted to the partial negative ($\delta -$) charge on the electronegative element. A good model set will permit you to build a model showing this effect and it can be particularly useful in understanding the double helix of DNA and the α-helix in proteins.

Line Structures

The type of structure you draw depends on what it is supposed to illustrate. Here are examples. The first emphasizes the atoms. It is a typesetter's notation because with a typewriter that is the best you can do. It is the style found in textbooks for that reason, but a chemist wouldn't draw it. We are interested in the bonds, and we are lazy. Besides, writing subscripts is a good way to get five bonds to carbon and that is strictly a no no, so by far the most common structures are abbreviated. A good rule to follow is that if you intend to use an atom or a bond, draw it out. Otherwise, abbreviate it.

Radical Chain Mechanisms

Radical reactions frequently begin with an unknown radical initiator: "In•" (with apologies to the element indium). In this abstract, the radical initiator is a halogen atom. It turns out that the bond between electronegative elements like the halogens, or oxygen, or a combination, is very weak and breaks to make radicals. In the mechanism, as long as one of the products has an unpaired electron, the radical chain is propagated. When all the electrons are paired, the chain is terminated.

Cyclic Structures

Regular polygons are commonly used for three-, four- and five-membered rings, but since the cyclohexane ring is puckered, that seems inappropriate. This abstract shows how to draw the cyclohexane ring correctly and how the axial and equatorial bonds are arranged. Notice which lines are parallel and which ones are not.

Orbitals and sp^2 Hybridization

The carbon-carbon double bond is fascinating. The σ-bond takes the shortest route between the carbons, while the π-bond wraps around it. It has to go around the σ-bond and this exposes two reactive faces. Syn addition will add substituents to the same face of the double bond and anti-addition adds one substituent to either face. This is known as the stereochemistry of the addition.

Alkenes - Addition and Elimination

Anti addition to a cis alkene gives a stereochemistry reminiscent of threose, a sugar. It is called "threo" in acyclic compounds. It would be trans in addition to a ring system. Elimination also favors anti stereochemistry. The E2 reaction is stereoselective because it happens so fast that the other atoms don't have a chance to move before the double bond is formed. Since a double bond inhibits rotation, the stereochemistry established during the reaction is preserved.

Alkenes - Anti-Markovnikov Addition

There are only two common reactions that give products with regiochemistry contrary to Markovnikov's rule. The combination of borane followed by alkaline hydrogen peroxide is one of these. The stereochemistry is syn, but the regiochemistry is anti-Markovnikov, and the mechanism is complicated.

Alkene Oxidation - Glycolization and Ozonolysis

Different reagents can oxidize an alkene to different extents. Since there are two different kinds of bonds σ and π, you might expect that some reagents would oxidize one and others both bonds. This is true. If it is kept cold and dilute $KMnO_4$ will oxidize only the π-system, but if it is allowed to get warm the concentrated solution will oxidize both the π- and the σ-bonds to give ketones and carboxylic acids. To get aldehydes, you must use reductive work-up on the ozonide. The conditions shown work best: dimethylsulfide, works better than zinc in aqueous acid for reducing an ozonide.

Hybrid Orbitals from Atomic Orbitals

Molecular orbital theory is too complicated to explain here, but the pictures say it all. If you add, or subtract, a 2s orbital and a 2p-orbital you get a pair of sp hybrid orbitals. Adding another 2p-orbital gives an sp^2 hybrid. Adding the third 2p-orbital exceeds my drawing skill, but it conveys the idea. In the diagram, lobes that are hashed in have the opposite sign of the ones that are open. Where they overlap, they cancel.

Conjugation - Molecular Orbitals vs. Resonance

Molecular orbital theory can be used to explain why the positive charge resides on the two carbons at the ends of the conjugated system in the allyl cation. If the electrons were added, they would flow into ϕ_2 and it has a node at the central atom, so the charge is on either end. MO theory is not needed, really, because resonance theory predicts the same result.

Benzene - Kekulé Structures and Hückel's Numbers

Aromatic compounds have Hückel's number of electrons (table) and a ring current. We will draw the circle in the ring if it stays unaltered during the reaction we are describing, but we draw the bonds in if they are involved. It is another case of emphasis versus laziness.

Electrophilic Aromatic Substitution

All electrophilic aromatic substitution reactions have the same mechanism: LA, LA, LA, etc. and then H^+. You may think I'm kidding, but I'm not. The reactions start with a Lewis Acid and continue until a proton is lost. Each intermediate is an electron deficient cation, so each is a Lewis Acid. Worse than that, the intermediates are not aromatic and will not be until the proton is lost.

Activating Groups (o,p directors)

All activating groups are good neighbors. They stabilize a positive charge on the atom attached to them. Alkyl (R-) groups stabilize by making the cation simultaneously tertiary and allylic, similarly aromatic (Ar-) groups make the cation benzylic as well as allylic, but the best activating groups have a lone pair that can participate via resonance. Aniline and phenol derivatives are the best. Halogens deactivate the ring because they are electronegative and pull electron density out of the ring.

Standard Mechanistic Steps

There are reactions that do not have intermediates called concerted reactions. There are reactions having intermediates that occur stepwise. These reactions can be classified according to the intermediates involved as radical or zwitterionic. Finally, zwitterionic reactions may be classified as anionic or cationic depending on the charge on the carbons of interest. It is rare for a reaction to switch from one type of mechanism to another, and writing a mechanism having an acid catalyst (cationic) in one part and a base catalyst (anionic) in another is almost always wrong. Choose a mechanistic set and stick with it. There are sixteen standard mechanistic steps and they are elaborated on another page. Look for them. These are the most important things I teach.

Chiral Molecules

The historical development of organic chemistry involves a select group of individuals. None is more important than Emil Fischer. Unfortunately, the Fischer projection must compete with the more modern structures and students have to learn both. This diagram shows how to convert from one to the other. Study it and practice until it comes easily for you.

Priority Rules (R & S and E & Z)

The Cahn, Ingold, and Prelog priority rules are used to specify R & S and E and Z. These are unambiguous rules and easily learned. Study them until they come easily to you. The most important thing is to remember to put the hydrogen in the back on a chiral center, and if a hydrogen is not one of the choices, then place the lowest priority group in the back. There is only one case where a hydrogen doesn't have the lowest priority... when one group is a lone pair. (No atom – no atomic number.)

Diasteriomers

Diasteriomers are stereoisomers that are not mirror images. That means that there is more than one chiral center, as in the example shown, or the diasteriomers are cis and trans alkenes. Meso compounds are tricky since they are their own mirror image. That means that each meso compound will reduce the number of diasteriomers possible by one. This fact makes for great "trick questions!" Watch for it.

S_N2 - Primary Alkyl Halides

The S_N2 reaction has a concerted mechanism. It leads to inversion of configuration and it works well on primary alkyl halides. These two ideas are incompatible because you cannot see inversion on primary carbons. You need secondary carbons for that and the SN2 really only works well for unhindered secondary carbons. So, watch for a reaction in which an acyclic alkyl halide goes from R to S or the reverse, or a cyclic system in which an alkyl halide goes from cis to trans.

Unimolecular S_N1

The S_N1 reaction involves a cation. Since primary cations do not form, the reaction is restricted to secondary and tertiary cases. The cation is planar (sp^2) and this arrangement permits a nucleophile to attack from either side, or face. That gives a stereorandom result in contrast to S_N2 which always gave inversion of configuration. Any time you see "1" as in S_N1 or E1 there will be a cation in the mechanism and the stereochemistry in the starting material will be lost

E1 and E2 - Alkene Stabilities

The cation intermediate present in an E1 mechanism can lose a proton from any carbon attached to it. Which one will be lost. The answer comes from Saytzeff's Rule of alkene stabilities. It turns out that the more substituted alkene is the most stable one. If the mechanism of alkene formation is concerted (E2) then the proton that can line up anti to the leaving group will be the one that is lost, and if possible the one leading to the trans alkene will be preferred.

Alcohols and Phenols as Acids and Bases

The rest of this abstract is devoted to showing that alcohols can be both acids and bases, and phenols are remarkably acidic because they exhibit both the inductive effect and the resonance effect. This conclusion is revealed by the pK_a values. An alcohol has a pK_a value like water (15.74) where the phenol is much more acidic. You can tell that the phenol is more acidic because the pK_a value is smaller. The pK_a value can go negative and for a mineral acid (inorganic acid like H_2SO_4) it is.

The Grignard Reaction

The Grignard reaction is a wonderful way to make carbon-carbon bonds. It is the best choice for making alcohols most of the time. Here are some examples where primary, secondary, and tertiary alcohols are products. In each case, carbons are added to the structure. Examine the flow of the electrons from the Grignard reagent (source) to the oxygen (sink). Grignard made a marvelous contribution. Remember to capitalize his name.

Balancing REDOX Equations

There are many ways to balance equations. This is one that will always work: Oxidation states are assigned to the carbon being oxidized by treating a hydrogen as if it were already a proton with a + charge, and oxygen has a charge of 2-. The number of electrons lost must equal the number of electrons gained before anything else can balance, and this is accomplished in the little box: The change in oxidation state is indicate by $\Delta\uparrow2$, meaning that two electrons were lost and the oxidation state went up. The change in oxidation state for the alcohol, in this example, becomes the fixed coefficient in front of the oxidizing agent, and vice versa. The fixed coefficients are not changed in the subsequent steps needed to balance the charges and atoms, and if everything is correct the hydrogens will balance without fail. Try it.

27

Retrons and Retrosynthetic Analysis

Sir Arthur Conan Doyle had the right idea about synthesis and analysis as we hear through the voice of his detective: Sherlock Holmes, in the passage from "A Study in Scarlet" quoted below. Holmes was the chemist. He speaks first, explaining his system to a well-educated, but rather slow-witted, Dr. Watson, who narrates in first-person.

"I have already explained to you that what is out of the common is usually a guide rather than a hindrance. In solving a problem of this sort, the grand thing is to be able to reason backward. That is a very useful accomplishment, and a very easy one, but people do not practice it much. In the everyday affairs of life it is more useful to reason forward, and so the other comes to be neglected. There are fifty who can reason synthetically for one who can reason analytically."

"I confess," said I, "that I do not quite follow you."

"I hardly expected that you would. Let me see if I can make it clearer. Most people, if you describe a train of events to them, will tell you what the result would be. They can put those events together in their mind, and argue from them that something will come to pass. There are few people, however, who, if you told them a result, would be able to evolve from their own inner consciousness what the steps were which led up to that result. This power is what I mean when I talk of reasoning backward, or analytically."

"I understand," said I.

"Now in this was a case in which you were given the result and had to find everything else for yourself. Now let me endeavour to show you the different steps in my reasoning...."

Multi-step synthesis problems are the bain of our existence in organic chemistry, but they also offer the greatest range of opportunities for creativity and satisfaction. To help you learn how to work a multi-step synthesis problem I have included a copy of "Synthesis Paradiso" and a list of suggestions, but before we do that I would like for you to consider this word game. Stork and Still are famous organic chemists from Columbia University in New York City. Devise a list of words that differ, each from the other, by only one letter and change STORK to STILL. Each word must be a real word and only one letter can be changed at a time. How would you work this problem? How many steps would it take? The best suggestion I can offer is that you should use the Scientific Method (Make a guess and see how it turns out, then make another guess.), and work the problem backward, analytically, (That way, you get to preserve any useful progress, since you know you can get from where you are to the end.). A multi-step synthesis is much the same. Each of the intermediate products has to be a real molecule, and it works best if only one change is made at a time. Syntheses that make lots of changes in a single step are either reckless or brilliant. Again, like the word game, it is best to work a synthesis problem backward. This brings us to Synthesis Paradiso and how to use it. The chart for Synthesis Paradiso resembles a road-map: the boxes are "pot-holes" for the reagent needed for the transformation and the arrows are the one-way roads that lead to the various destinations. The chart is generic. It is not exhaustive. There are many reagents left out, but it still gives a useful starting place. Synthesis Paradiso can be used in two different ways: (1) It can be used as a drill to keep fresh the information you have already learned; or, (2) It can help in designing a synthesis. For example, suppose you were faced with the prospect of making an ester from an alkane. How would you proceed? Well, it would be well to find the box for esters and look at the routes leading to it. Trace them backward to the various starting materials. Pick the one that looks best, and repeat the process (Scientific Method) until you find the route that leads to an alkane. Then, if you know how to fill in the "pot-holes" you have a multi-step, road-map synthesis. The difference is that your ester will have a specific structure (Concrete thinking) where Synthesis Paradiso is generic (Formal thinking).

Using the Chemical Literature: Chemical Abstracts

Chemical Abstracts provides the best and most complete entry into the chemical literature. Most often, you will have some information before you start. I usually give my students the name and structure of the compound, the author's name and the approximate year of publication. In my research, I am lucky if I know anything more than the structure of the compound. There are various indices in Chem. Abstracts, and in the worked example, I have shown entries from the Chemical Substance Index, the Author Index, and the Formula index. I was looking for Macrostomine synthesized by Seebach in 1980, and look at the trouble I had! You will have similar difficulties, but the information is sure to be there.

After you find the original article, you can trace the synthesis of the starting materials back to dirt, if you want to. In my classes, I usually encourage my students to trace the synthesis back to something that is commercially available (Aldrich Catalog). This gives a clear perspective on the state of organic chemistry today. With enough demand to support the production of all the compounds in that catalog, you begin to realize that the subject you are studying is real.

Synthesis Paradiso

Synthesis Paradiso

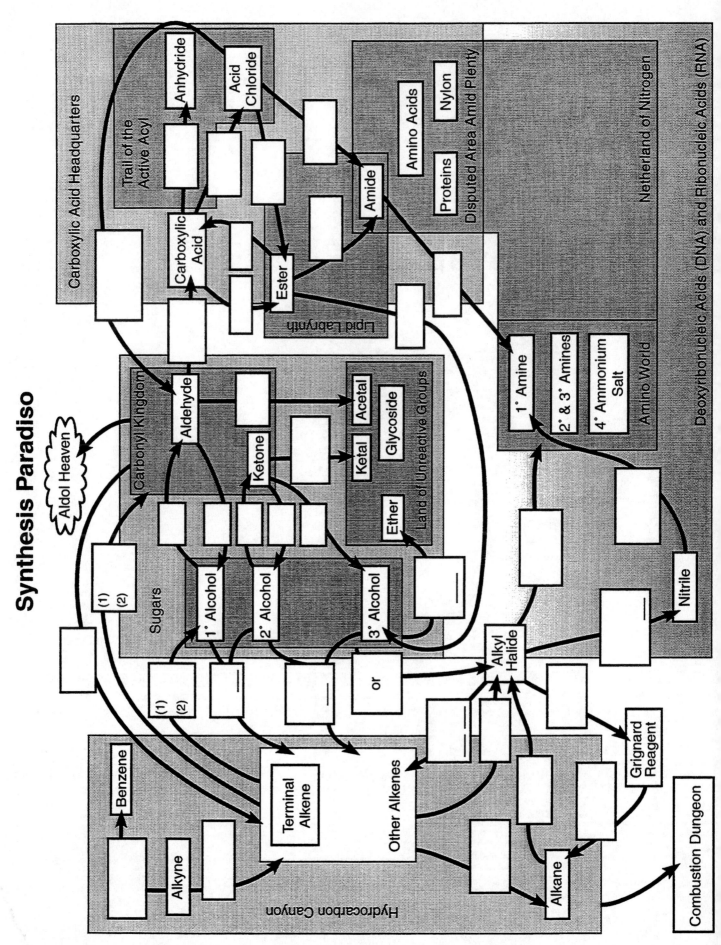

Synthesis Paradiso

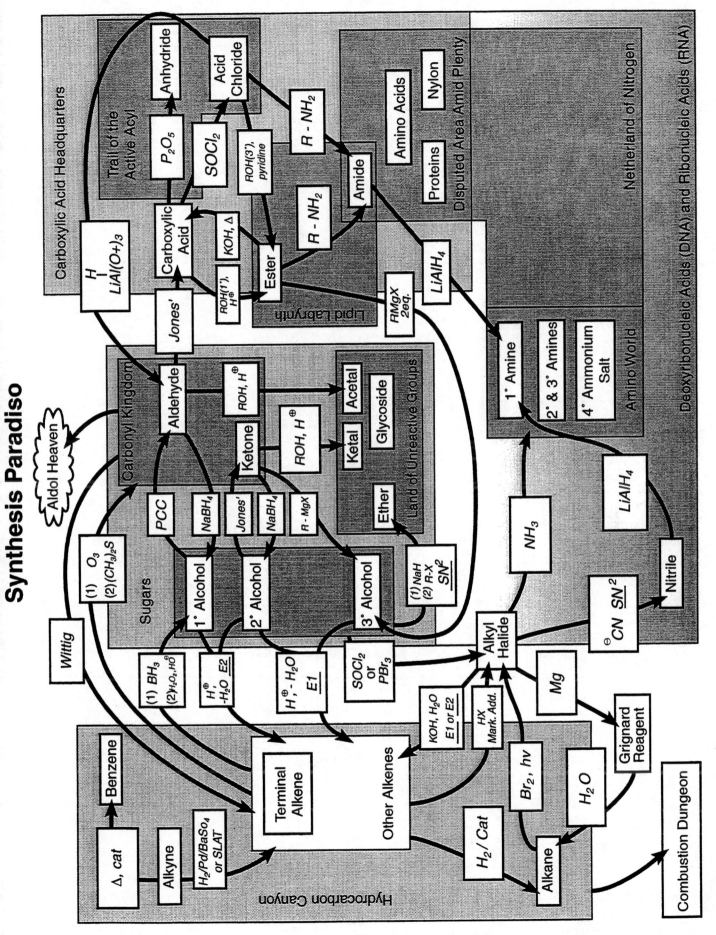

A worked example: **Macrostomine – Seebach 1980:**

Formula Index: $C_{24}H_{26}N_2O_6$

**Isoquinoline, 1-((1,3-benzodioxol-5-ylmethyl)-6,0-
7-dimethoxy-4-(1-methyl-2-pyrrolidinyl)-
(±)- [76023-36-4], 94: 15934x
(S)- [53912-94-0], 87: 85158b, 114659y; 90:
23342k; 93: 128757q**

— Correct citation

No entry

The Chemical Abstract

94: 15934x A nitrosamine route to (±)-macrostomine.
Wykypiel, Werner; Seebach, Dieter (Lab. Org. Chem., ETH-Zentrum,
CH-8092 Zurich, Switz.). *Tetrahedron Lett.* 1980, 21(20),
1927–30 (Eng). Macrostomine (I), the main alkaloid of *Papaver*

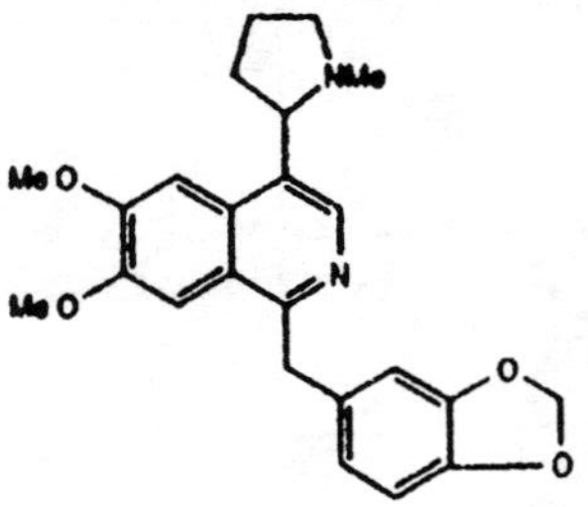

macrostomum, was prepd. from the tetrahydroisoquinoline II in
10 steps. In the main steps, both side chains of the isoquinoline
group were alkylated, by high yield C–C bond formation with
lithiated nitrosamines.

The Journal Article

A NITROSAMINE ROUTE TO (±)-MACROSTOMINE

Werner Wykypiel[a] and Dieter Seebach[b]

No entry

Chemical Substance Index

Macronil *[73561-93-0]*
  bactericidal action of, animal growth in relation to,
  92: 191197b
Macrophage insulin-like activity *[71343-61-8]*
  glucose oxidn. by adipose tissue in response to, 91:
  121100v
Macrotetrolide *[75366-98-2]*
  degrdn. of, by soil. 93: 23268?c

No entry

Author Index

Seebach, Dieter See Amstutz, Rene; Beck, Albert K.;
  Bock, Hans; Buerstinghaus, Rainer; Colvin, Ernest
  W.; Dammann, Reinhard; Enders, Dieter; Geiss,
  Karl Heinz; Gieller, Jean Claude; Gray, Robert
  William; Groebel, Bengt Thomas; Hassel, Tillmann;
  Hungerbuehler, Ernst; Kalinowski, Hans Otto;
  Knochel, Paul; Langer, Werner; Lehr, Friedrich;
  Locher, Ria; Lohmann, Jean Jacques; Lubosch,
  Winfried; Meyer, Norbert; Neumann, Helmut;
  Nitsche, Manfred; Paulsen, Hans; Pohlemann,
  Heinz; Pohmakotr, Manat; Renger, Bernd; Schlecker,
  Rainer; Schmidt, Manfred; Seuring, Bernhard;
  Siegel, Herbert; Weidmann, Beat; Weller, Thomas;
  Wykypiel, Werner; Wykypiel, Werner; Zuger, Max
  Reactivity umpolung methods, 90: 185829b
——; Beck, A. K.; Lehr, F.; Weller, T.; Colvin, E. W.
  Diastereoselective synthesis of β-nitro- and β-amino
  alcohols, 95: 80021j
——; Buerstinghaus, R.; Groebel, B. T.; Kolb, M.
  Polarity reversal of carbonyl reactivity; N2/E1 and
  N4/E1 reactions of 1,1-dihetero substituted olefins
  and dienes, 87: 152093a

— Other authors

——; Colvin, E. W.; Lehr, F.; Weller, T.
  Nitroaliphatic compounds — ideal intermediates in
  organic synthesis, 90: 120460e
——; Crass, G.; Wilka, Eva M.; Hilvert, Don; Brunner,
  F.di

No entry

Wykpiel, Werner — Misspelled Name
——; Seebach, D.
  A nitrosamine route to (±)-macrostomine, 94: 15934x
Wykpiez, Audrey Chou
  Ultrafiltration system for latex paint wastewater
  treatment. 95: 29739v
Wykrent, Cezimir See Filous, Jiri; Nemecek, Petr
Wykrota, Wieslaw See Mokrzycki, Eugeniusz
Wykurz, J., See Celejowa, I.
Wykypiel, Werner See Renger, Bernd; Seebach,
  Dieter
——; Lohmann, J. J.; Seebach, D.
  Lithiation in α-position to the N-atom of
  triphenylacetamides from cyclic secondary amines.
  Rearrangement of metalated triphenylacetamides by
  1,3-shift of carbamoyl groups, 95: 16821?d ....

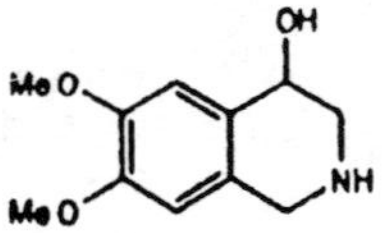

Correct citation

Correct name

Poem

Roses are:

(red)

Cornflowers:

You should know that metal
Might be Zn (II).